Love's Open Door

By Anne Pierson

Loving and Caring, Inc.
www.lovingandcaring.org

Love's Open Door

By Anne Pierson

© 2015 Loving and Caring, Inc.
www.lovingandcaring.org

ISBN-10: 0-9861773-0-X
SBN-13: 978-0-9861773-0-9

Printed in the United States of America

Dedication

This book is dedicated to Jimmy,
my wonderful husband for 51 years.
He was an amazing father to those given him
through birth and those who came through our doors.

Acknowledgments

A very special thanks goes to all the young women who have graced my life with their presence as well as my own children who embraced all those who came through our doors. Holly, Shelly you are both amazing children and are carrying on the care of others in your own lives. Thank you to Ruth Morris for helping me write out this journey.

"Let the message of Christ dwell among you richly as you teach and admonish one another with all wisdom through psalms, hymns, and songs from the Spirit, singing to God with gratitude in your hearts. And whatever you do, whether in word or deed, do it all in the name of the Lord Jesus, giving thanks to God the Father through him."

Colossians 3:16-18

Contents

"But no stranger had
to spend the night in the street,
for my door was always
open to the traveler"

Job 31:32

Chapter 1

Melissa

The July breeze set the curtains swaying and carried the sounds of teenagers at play into my kitchen. It was a song rich in harmony. The smack of volleyball serves blended with enthusiastic cheers and light-hearted boos as first one side, then the other, gained the advantage. My husband Jim's voice boomed like a kettledrum as he teased, encouraged, joked, and urged them on in their boisterous play. It was Monday evening—time for the weekly meeting of our church youth group, nicknamed "The Family."

Soon they would troop into the house for Bible study and fellowship but not until an undisputed victor had been declared on the volleyball court. And certainly not before Jim had squeezed out every drop of possible enjoyment. It was this gift for making the most of every opportunity to play that fitted him so well to the role of youth advisor. His father-heart welcomed the teens into a shelter of uncritical love and acceptance and, in turn, they provided him with an enthusiastic audience for his clowning and practical jokes.

Meanwhile, I thrived on the teaching opportunities, excited by all the possibilities for growth and maturity for these young people. As a stay-at-home mom with two small girls, one of whom was handicapped, The Family helped me keep a broader view of life—there was more in my world than the weekly doctor appointments and therapy sessions. Jim and I loved teenagers, so The Family gave us a perfect way to serve the Lord while thoroughly enjoying ourselves. How I loved my own children and those young people God had entrusted to me.

I hurried through the last of the dishes so I could join in the fun. Put the saucepan away…hang up the tea towel…complete silence…wipe the counter…hey, what happened to the noise? The rollicking song in the backyard had stopped, as if the volume knob had been switched to "off." Before I could look out the window, the door swung open, bouncing against the wall. Jennie, a youth group regular, rushed into the kitchen supporting an unfamiliar girl. Arm protectively placed around her shoulders, Jennie said, "I think we are going to need first aid, Anne. Melissa just got slammed in the face by the ball."

Covering the sudden tightening in my stomach with what I hoped was a confident smile and cheery, "Let's have a look," I led her to the nearest chair.

Melissa slipped into it with a muffled groan and tilted her head up so I could better examine the damage. A red bump straddled the bridge of her nose, puffiness spread towards brow and cheek. The only other signs of damage were the bent wire rim glasses dangling from Melissa's hand.

The knot in my stomach unraveled. "How about getting some ice on that nose? If we're lucky we might be able to prevent any more swelling." I smiled and stepped back. She nodded agreement and tucked pale curly blonde hair behind her ear. It was only then that I noticed one other swelling: the young lady sitting in front of me was obviously several months pregnant. I could feel a few strands of my former knot twisting back together.

I reached for the ice cubes. Well, Anne, how are you going to respond to that? Mention it? Pretend you didn't notice? What on earth was she doing playing volleyball? Better wait and see if someone else brings it up. Using a plastic bag and a dishtowel, I improvised an ice pack. Gently laying it on Melissa's nose produced a smile and a whispered "thank you."

I should talk to her… What do I say? A sudden surge of teens erupting into the kitchen rescued me from my dilemma—at least temporarily. Hot, sweaty bodies swirled around Melissa all talking at once.

"Hey, Melissa, you okay?"

"I'm sorry. I didn't mean to hit it so hard."

"Hope you're not hurt."

"Did you break your glasses?"

Reassured that no permanent damage had been done, The Family, in a whirlwind of energy, swept on into the living room carrying Melissa with it. There it found a new source of release in guitar-strumming, hand-clapping worship. I followed more slowly, preoccupied with unanswered questions. Who is she? Where did she come from? Who did she come with? She looks like such a shy, good girl, not the kind I expect to get pregnant without being married. It was 1970, and I thought only wild types got into this kind of trouble.

The only sound was the ice cubes chattering in the glasses of tea. Melissa, her face a deep pink, hunched in one corner of our sofa. Head down, hands entangled and white-knuckled, she glanced at Jennie. Silence—like a balloon swollen and ready to pop—pinned us in our chairs.

"The Family" had left thirty minutes ago, but Jennie and Melissa had found reasons to stay: the living room to straighten, snacks to put away, pillows to fluff. An invitation to iced tea was quickly accepted, and we found ourselves making chit chat until I decided to drag the lurking issue out of its cave and into the middle of the living room, "You're pregnant aren't you, Melissa?"

And for the longest minute, all we heard was the soft clatter of ice rubbing against ice.

With a sigh, Melissa straightened and looked at me. "Yes."

"What are your plans?"

"I've been in touch with a maternity home here in D.C. I'm supposed to move in in a few weeks." As she blinked, a single tear escaped and slid down her cheek. "After the baby is born, they'll find someone who wants to adopt…"

She stared at her hands watching them twist and untwist. Twice her lips parted as if to speak, and twice she stopped. Moistening her lips she tried for the third time. The words whispered so low and soft I leaned forward to hear them, "I don't want to marry the baby's father, and I don't think I can take care of a baby all by myself." The words tore her fragile composure into frayed pieces. Sobs began to shudder from deep within while tears smeared her cheeks and dripped from her chin.

I turned to Jim hoping he would know what to say. But words wouldn't be coming from him any time soon. At the first sign of Melissa's tears, his eyes grew moist. Her sobs must have tightened his throat—all he could do was swallow… and swallow… and swallow. (Jim carries nearly three hundred pounds on a six-foot-four-football-center frame, but he's about as tough as dandelion fuzz. His heart is quickly and easily touched by someone's pain.) But no amount of tears could blur his message. Like many couples with years of marriage who had truly grown to understand each other, I knew without words what he was thinking. It was the same thought that had popped uninvited into my mind. But how do you lead up to that idea, Anne? You can't just spring it on her.

Now even the ice cubes were still. The harder I tried to think of something to say, the less my brain had to suggest. I needed wisdom and it went into hiding. I searched for words of encouragement, and they vacated the premises. My mouth, impatient with the delay, bypassed my brain and assumed control of the situation. "Would you rather come here to stay with us, Melissa?"

Melissa's head snapped up as she searched first my face, then Jim's. A hesitant smile appeared and slowly spread as she admitted, "I really do think I'd like that very much."

Anne, what have you done! Inviting a stranger into your home. I turned to Jim for reassurance. Beaming a smile that nearly split his face in two and nodding vigorous agreement, he had no doubts.

And so the decision was made, and our life's course was forever altered. Melissa, aged 18, would move in with us in one week. The ways, means, and timetable for this life-changing decision were discussed and agreed upon before they left that same evening.

Later as we headed for bed, my brain, like the last loop in a stretched-out Slinky™, finally caught up. Why isn't Melissa going home to her family in Cleveland? Do they know she is pregnant? Why a maternity home in a strange city? Why didn't she want to marry the father? Anne, you know practically nothing beyond her name and age-- who have you invited into your home? What kind of influence will she have on our children? What will Grandpa think?

Looking around our bedroom set my mind reeling in another direction. We had only three small bedrooms—this one, the one shared by our daughters Holly, aged eight, and Shelly, aged five, and my eighty-eight-year-old Grandpa's room. "Jim, where will she sleep? There's no room!"

"Don't worry. We'll find space for her somewhere," was Jim's reply along with a nonchalant shrug.

"Where, Jim?" exasperation and panic put a strident edge in my voice. "She can't sleep on the floor in her condition."

Jim scratched his head, "Well," he drawled, "There's the sofa." That settled to his satisfaction, he slid into bed, pulled the sheet up, and turned onto his side. Meanwhile I mentally tucked Melissa in our sofa – and winced. Tired and worn, it had long ago forgotten the meaning of support. But where else could we put her?

"Okay," I conceded, "the sofa might work, but what about Melissa's family? Shouldn't we contact them? After all, she is only 18." Jim's only response was a gentle snore. He had dared to fall asleep right in the middle of my crisis.

I considered waking him up. No, the commitment is made. For better or worse, we are about to become surrogate-grandparents-in-waiting. Fussing and fretting won't do any good. With a resigned chuckle I climbed into bed and snuggled next to my slumbering husband. Our house wasn't the biggest or best, our credentials non-existent, but we did have a family eager to love and support Melissa through the birth of her child. As for what we lacked, God had custom-designed prayer for those very situations. Let the adventure begin.

To think about

- It is easy to put people in boxes and stereotype them according to their sins just as I did with Melissa. Those boxes limit our ability to reach out and minister. What boxes do you need to dismantle? Matthew 7: 1-5 (NIV) says it this way: "Do not judge, or you too will be judged. For in the same way you judge others, you will be judged, and with the same measure you use, it will be measured to you. Why do you look at the speck of sawdust in your brother's eye and pay no attention to the plank in your own eye? How can you say to your brother, 'Let me take the speck out of your eye,' when all the time there is a plank in your own eye? You hypocrite, first take the plank out of your own eye, and then you will see clearly to remove the speck from your brother's eye." From God's perspective, judging someone else is a plank-size sin compared to the other person's speck-size sin.

- "God does not ask about our ability or inability, but about our availability." Jim and I would have missed twenty-five incredible years of loving and helping if we had focused on our inabilities. What is God nudging you to do that will push you past your comfort zone and into the adventure zone?

- Have you used excuses to make yourself unavailable? Follow Jim's example: take everything in stride, knowing God will put all the pieces together. Don't let fear rob you of the joy of fulfilling God's plans and purposes for your life.

"Jesus looked at them and said,
'With man this is impossible,
but not with God; all things
are possible with God.'"

Mark 10:27

Chapter 2

The Birth

"And when that 'canned' music started, Jim grabbed Holly and began waltzing her down the aisles of K-Mart! She's giggling and other customers are laughing and clapping…"

"He's so much fun," Melissa rummaged through a cluttered drawer in our church's kitchen.

"He's wonderful!"

"Yes, I wish… Anne, can I tell you something?"

I stopped stirring the soup to give her my full attention. In the past month she had slowly, hesitantly shared bits and pieces of her past. As if building a house of cards, she placed each new fact on the structure of our relationship with extreme caution and stifled breath, pausing to see if the whole thing would stand or collapse. As we received each new revelation with gentle and matter-of-fact acceptance, the house stood. But if we had reacted with disgust and horror, the house would have fallen, never to be rebuilt: my shock would have sent her scuttling back inside herself, too hurt to build again.

It hadn't been easy to hold back my gasp of dismay when she told me that since coming to D.C. to train as a legal secretary she had had casual sex with a young man she barely knew. It was hard not to let a judgmental attitude seep through when she described her mother's home—dirty dishes piled on the counter and in the sink, rabbit trails winding through the living room between stacks of discarded newspapers, and more.

(After her parents' divorce, her mother had grown discouraged and disinterested—keeping house was just too much work.) Melissa, too embarrassed to invite friends home, always had them drop her off at the end of the street to make sure they never saw the shambles of a once immaculate home.

It took more self-control than I thought I had to show only concern when she described the fights she and her mother had had over her move to D.C. "Then I went and did exactly what Mom was afraid I'd do," Melissa had confessed. "I tried out everything I hadn't been allowed to do back home. I went to every party even though there was a lot of drinking and smoking pot, sex…I wanted so much to belong." It certainly wasn't easy to keep the judgment out of my expression when I learned that Melissa's mother had offered no help and had made it clear she could not go home to have her child.

Just remember whatever she tells you, you can sort through your emotions later. Don't damage her trust by reacting negatively while she is watching.

"Anne, my baby's father…he's not a bit like Jim," she began. Her slender body with that one preposterous bulge bent over the drawer as if finding the can opener ranked right behind discovering a cure for cancer. "I mean not at all like Jim…in fact," her hands stilled… "in fact, he's…he's black."

Her head tilted to one side, peeping through a curtain of blonde hair, she watched me from the corner of her eye.

Oh, my. Be careful, Anne. Help, God. What do I say?

The answer came into my heart, settled and immovable: "Melissa, God loves your baby just as much as any baby in this world.

And so do we." Tears filled her reddened rims and meandered down the side of her nose. Forehead pressed against a cabinet, she absorbed the words. Finally, she turned to me... Baby sandwiched between us, we hugged and cried together.

Thank you, Lord. I would have made a total mess of this on my own. Help me never to hurt a wounded child by reacting in my emotions, innocence, or even ignorance. I will start praying right now for a very special couple to adopt this precious little one—parents who are not looking at skin color.

Although the civil rights movement had made big changes in our culture by 1970, biracial relationships were not considered acceptable and neither were the children.

The first "thump" blended into my dream of a room packed wall-to-wall with infants—laughing, gurgling, cooing, crying moppets waving rattles and banging bottles against the floor. The hollow "bump" and Melissa's voice calling me tore a small hole in my dream fabric allowing the Technicolor™ images of squirming babies with very dirty diapers to seep away.

"An-nn-ne," a giggle in the middle broke my name into three syllables. Hastily pushing myself onto my elbows, I searched the room. Melissa's voice had sounded so close, but all I saw in the early morning dimness was the small shadowy lump of Shelly sleeping in the cot next to our dresser and the man-mountain beside me. "Melissa, where are you?"

Another giggle, a muffled snort, and toenails scrambling on the wood floor were all the clues I needed. Jennifer, our English bulldog, like the last employee hired, had been "bumped" from her favorite sleeping spot to make room for Shelly's cot. Determined to sleep in our room, she snoozed in the doorway—a low hurdle for anyone coming or going.

The cot was the answer to my rather vague and unfocused prayer: God, Melissa has no privacy sleeping on the couch. The early morning traffic through our living room qualified as moderate to heavy, located as it was at the intersection of stairs, kitchen, and front door. But there's no other place to put her, Lord.

The cot had arrived via friends at church. Too small for Melissa, it was just right for Shelly. It had taken less than a week for my fears about Melissa's influence on my girls and grandpa to evaporate—disappearing in the warmth of her smile and her eagerness to help. So when the cot was offered, I was ready to receive it. Melissa would share Holly's room while Shelly, squirming with delight, snuggled down in the cot.

"Melissa, are you all right?"

"I'm fine. But I think I'm in labor."

By this time Jim was groggily searching for the light switch. In the island of lamp glow, I saw Melissa sitting on the floor grinning sheepishly while gently scratching Jennifer's ears. Spraddle-legged and bewildered, the dog snorted her confusion. I understood her feelings exactly. What had Melissa said?

Labor! The word propelled Jim and me out of bed even though it was only 5 am. Pulling on the first clothes we found… "How close are the pains?" … "About 20 minutes or so..." Jim and I came up with a plan—he would make tea while I settled Melissa on the couch and timed her contractions.

Five…six…seven. Melissa winced, squeezed my hand, then relaxed. Worry blurred the edges of her smile, "Wow, that was the biggest one yet."

"Talking about me, again," Jim joked, coming from the kitchen juggling two cups of steaming tea.

"Did you hear that, Anne? Jim just called himself a pain."

Melissa's chuckle sparkled in her eyes and shook the tension from her back. "Mmm, the tea is perfect." Hands curled around the comforting warmth, Melissa sipped and relaxed… "Uh, oh, here we go again."

"The contractions are getting closer." Tea abandoned on the coffee table, Jim and Melissa headed for the hospital. I stayed behind to make phone calls and organize emergency help on the home front.

Less than an hour later, after my mother arrived to be with Grandpa and watch the girls, I headed toward the hospital in our tired, old van.

Movie clips of the last six weeks replayed in my mind. Melissa's assorted stuffed animals packed around Victorian lamps and "doo-dads"…her reserve battered by my girls' enthusiasm …Jim's zany pranks—Melissa must have felt bewildered and alien. Face it, Anne, the Pierson world—unpredictable, crowded, and boisterous—is not your normal household.

It had taken about a week before Melissa, nicknamed Minnie Mouse and designated first assistant of practical jokes, relaxed and in the process revealed a well-developed sense of humor. It had been Jim, of course, with his special gift for drawing people out of themselves who had helped her feel at home so quickly.

My memory movie moved on to other scenes. Melissa and Grandpa watching TV westerns together… Holly and Melissa making a game of cleaning the bathroom…Shelly sitting on Melissa's lap chattering away convinced that Melissa was hanging on her every word…Jim whispering fresh instructions for mischief in her ear—gleeful anticipation spilling over like shaken soda… Melissa and I at the kitchen table sipping tea and sharing dreams and memories. She had found a place in our home and hearts, her laughter woven into our family fabric. But soon she would no longer need us; the birth behind her, she would leave us and return to her plans for the future. What a hole that would create in our lives.

Clunk…thump…clunk. The van shuddered to a stop, using the last of its momentum to coast to the curb. Lord, not now! Turning the key produced nothing—not a single whimper. Jim can't stay with Melissa; he'll be late for work. How am I going to get to the hospital? It's not even six in the morning…Wait a minute…This neighborhood looks familiar…

My panic subsided a little as I realized a friend's house was less than a block away. Scrambling from the van, I jogged toward the dark house. Never mind that they were obviously still asleep—I needed help. Thank You, Lord. If the van had to die, this is the perfect spot for it to happen.

Five minutes to explain why I was standing on their porch in breathless panic, another five for them to dress and find car keys, and I was on my way once more. How wonderful to have true friends I can go to for help.

Lord, Melissa's going to think I've deserted her. Comfort her until I can get there…

"But her parents aren't here. She's been living with Jim and me." Panic made my voice sharp.

"No one but family is allowed in maternity." The nurse, as starchy as her uniform, was not budging.

"She needs someone with her. She's all alone."

"It is against policy to allow you in her room."

"Can you at least tell me how she's doing?"

Just short of rolling her eyes in exasperation, the nurse glanced at a clipboard and said, "Both she and the baby are satisfactory."

"Boy or girl?"

Frowning, she consulted her clipboard, "It does not say."

Lord, how am I supposed to get in? I need help here. The more I prayed the greater my sense of urgency and determination.

"I must see Melissa. What is her room number?"

"Mrs. Pierson, our rules do not permit visitors other than family."

"Who made the rule and why?"

"I don't know."

"Where is it written?"

"I don't know."

"So you are following a rule that isn't written down. What room is she in?"

"Mrs. Pierson, I must follow policy…"

"I insist…"

After measuring my determination against her standard procedures, she muttered, "Room 325."

Not giving her time to change her mind, I hurried toward Melissa's room. Pausing in the doorway, I searched the beds for her.

I followed the sounds of muffled sobbing to the last one. "They won't let me see my baby, Anne," Melissa whispered. "They said it's the rule because I'm placing him in adoption. Please, Anne, I want to hold my baby."

Pausing only long enough to give her a reassuring hug, I strode back out to find the nurse with the rulebook. She was horrified at the idea—it was absolutely out of the question. I persisted, refusing to back down or go away. Finally with a huff of indignation and a warning that I was making a big mistake, she sent an aide to bring Melissa's child to her.

Is it a mistake, Lord? I hope not! But it seems to me that she can't say "good-bye" before she's said "hello."

Melissa beamed from ear to ear. "Just look at him. Isn't he something?" Nestled in her arms was a slumbering infant. We stared in awe at the shining curls tumbling about his head…the sooty lashes brushing dusky cheeks…hands, dimpled and tucked in tiny fists…a mouth, no bigger than a petal, making little sucking noises.

"Oh, you are beautiful," she crooned, pulling the blanket cocoon closer and kissing him gently on his forehead. "I'm going to call him, Adam. Don't you think he looks like an Adam?"

Tears pooled in my eyes as I watched her cuddling the baby and murmuring words of love. This is the baby she is giving up for adoption? How? Now that she's seen him, held him, kissed him… How will she be able to part with him? How does any mother do it? Where do they find the strength and determination to let beautiful, loved babies go?

To think about

- Adventures with God only happen outside our comfort zone. Think about the times He has nudged you to help someone in need even though it means moving outside your safe, familiar environment and taking a risk. What happened?

- The more we open our world to enfold another, the more likely it is that we will find truly wonderful relationships. The risk comes before the reward. What fears or concerns keep you from enfolding others?

- Jesus assured us that, "With God all things are possible." (Matthew 19:26) What needs do you have that are so big and overwhelming only God can turn them into "possibles?"

"A father to the fatherless,
a defender of widows,
is God in his holy dwelling."

Psalm 68:5

Chapter 3

Loving and Letting Go

"I just can't sign any papers until I'm sure I'm doing the right thing." Tears seeped from under reddened lids, forming rivulets that ran unchecked down Melissa's cheeks. Dark circles smudged her high cheekbones while worry lines etched her forehead—motherhood was aging Melissa beyond her eighteen years.

"Maybe adoption is the best choice, but I'm not sure yet. I have to be absolutely certain I'm giving Adam the best possible future."

Lord, this is what I was afraid would happen...There is so little I can do to help...I hate to see her hurting so.

With a sigh as deep as her toes, Melissa leaned her head against the van's window and watched D. C. traffic. Adam was three days old today, and Melissa was coming home –alone. That oh-so-sensible and mature adoption plan she had carefully crafted while Adam was a nebulous little "someone" was on hold because now Adam had chocolate brown eyes, silky black curls and dimpled hands. Adam was a person. Adam was a beloved son. And Melissa was no longer certain she could let him go.

On the advice of Julie Howe, Melissa's social worker from the Department of Children and Youth, Adam was in temporary foster care while Melissa sorted out her fears, struggled to find a solution that gave her peace, and faced the pain that comes with a love big enough to let him go.

"That way you are free to work through your choices without the pressure and emotional pull of caring for Adam," Julie had said.

Thank you, Lord, for Julie. Her experience and wisdom have been a real lifeline. I'm so glad Melissa had contacted her. I was beginning to suspect that Jim and I would need the time as well. Adam is so lovable. How can we say "good-bye?" Already the thought of never seeing him again made my heart ache. And thank you, Lord, for her counsel to me—although I think she was preparing me for the worst case scenario...

"Melissa won't reach a decision in a day or two. You need to be prepared, Anne, for this process to take several weeks," she had warned.

A traffic light gave me a chance to reach over and squeeze her hand, stilling for a moment its aimless motion. "Take all the time you need. We love having you in our family."

"Thanks. First I want to look for an efficiency apartment and a job. Maybe I can keep him...I've got to try. Maybe," her mind searched for ideas no matter how improbable, "if my mom sees him, she'll love him. How could anyone not love him? We could raise him together. Or my best friend, she loves children. We could get an apartment together..."

Help, Lord! Do I encourage her? Throw some cold reality water on her ideas? Those mother instincts are really kicking in. Should I interfere? Help? Keep my mouth shut?

The notepad was blank, the newspaper pages no longer rustled, and Melissa stared at our kitchen wall, sipping hot tea grown cold. For weeks she had searched for a miracle apartment—a safe place within her price range and a matching miracle job that would supply a living wage—one that came without experience or educational prerequisites. Each day she sat down with determination and hope. Each day she folded the paper with trembling lips and slumping shoulders.

"I suppose I knew all along it wasn't possible. Rent's too high. Wages for unskilled work too low...I shouldn't have wasted all this time dreaming."

She folded the paper with finality, pushed away from the table, and trailed upstairs to her bedroom.

It's so hard to watch hopes die. Surely there is something we can do.

"You know we have all that unused space in our basement," Jim's comment picked up right where my thoughts had stopped.

"Fix up an apartment?"

"It'd be small, but big enough for Melissa and Adam."

"How much would it cost?"

"Not sure. I'll check on prices tomorrow."

A couple of days later Melissa caught us working on sketches and rough estimates. Shaking her head so emphatically her hair swung out in an arch, she said, "I could never allow you to do that. I'd love to be part of your family forever, but you've already sacrificed enough for me."

"But you wouldn't have to place Adam."

"And I don't want to place him." Her words came slowly, impeded by the ball of tears in her throat. "I love him so much it hurts, but it wouldn't be fair to your or the girls or Grandpa to tear your home apart for me. Somehow I have to work this out for myself."

Days passed while she searched for a solution and cried with every option that disappeared. Before Adam was born, she had spent hours at our piano filling our house with classical music. Now she rarely played, and then only until tears overwhelmed her. Even though she tried to muffle the sobs, the sound carried through the bedroom walls. The incredible creativity that had spilled over in poems, watercolors and calligraphy, was washed away in a river of tears.

Five weeks and still Melissa hadn't found a choice she could live with. Her pain and despair touched everything—it was an invisible guest at every meal, an intruder we could not ignore.

"I want to call Mom. Ask her what to do," Melissa announced in a subdued whisper.

She's really getting desperate now. After the way her mother responded to news of her pregnancy…

"No, you may not come home to have that baby. You made your choices. Now you can live with the consequences," her mother's voice had been filled with icy resolve the day Melissa had told her about the baby.

It hadn't always been that way. Before her father left to marry someone else, Melissa's had been a normal home with a warm supportive mother and a beloved daddy. That had all changed with her father's desertion. Feeling abandoned and confused she had turned to her mother, but her mother had withdrawn into her own world of heartache. More and more she had become preoccupied with discipline and spotless reputations.

"I had to take care of myself," she said. And for the most part she hadn't done too badly. But now her desire to keep Adam over-rode past hurts and rejections; she was ready to ask her mother for help. Even after the decision was made it took her several days to find the courage to call...

"Anne, would you pray for me. I want to have the right attitude when I talk to my mother. And I need to know what to say and how to say it."

"I'd be delighted. Father, Melissa needs Your help. Work in her heart so that her attitudes are pure. And give her the right words when she talks to her mother. Just wrap her in Your love."

With a smile of thanks, Melissa left the kitchen to make her phone call in private. Thirty minutes later she returned. Feet dragging she slumped into a chair and sagged as if her shoulders carried fifty pound weights.

Oh no. How can a mother be so hard? Doesn't she know how much her rejection hurts?

Empty eyes stared at me from Melissa's face. Her gray, pinched features alarmed me. As I sat across from her, silently grieving, searching for words of comfort and hope, she spoke, "Mom said she was glad to hear from me but she didn't offer to help. She didn't want to hear about Adam or see him...I'm so tired."

That evening we couldn't coax her to the dinner table, and according to Holly, she sobbed quietly into her pillow throughout the night.

"I'm going to call Dad," Melissa declared just a few days later.

Love certainly gives us the courage and determination to face some pretty overwhelming situations. She's ready to face rejection again.

She returned just ten minutes later answering my raised eyebrow with a shake of her head. "Maybe this is God's way of letting me know that I need to let Adam go," she said. "If He is closing doors, it must mean He has something else for my baby."

Lord, her words sound so mature, so responsible—her head is clear, but I didn't hear her heart agreeing. She needs to know in her heart that this is Your plan.

Later that afternoon Melissa visited Adam at his foster home. Warm and cuddly, Adam wrapped pudgy fingers around her heart and squeezed. Tears and indecision followed her home.

The next morning over our cups of tea, she began to share her fears. "What if Adam thinks I didn't love him? That he wasn't wanted?" Tears spilling over as she continued, "One of the aides at the hospital said she couldn't imagine a mother with so little love that she'd give her baby to someone else." Hands smearing wet cheeks, she paused to draw a shuddering breath, "Do you think Adam will grow up believing I didn't love him?"

Of all the insensitive busybodies ...no wonder she's torn. "Any sensible adoptive parents would want Adam to see that you gave him a better life because you did love him so much. No Christian parents would want their child to feel rejected and abandoned."

"But that's the problem," her hands tightened around the teacup with white knuckled intensity. "I can't be sure his parents will be Christian. Julie says she can put it on the application papers. And she will try to see that it is honored. But she can't promise. If I knew Adam's parents would be like you and Jim, I'd feel so much better about letting him go."

Better not tell her Jim and I had talked about taking Adam ourselves. A son... what a wonderful thought. How Jim and I longed for more children, especially a son. We already loved Adam. The longing became so strong Jim and I began to seriously pray about adopting Adam. We struggled to give the longing for Adam back to the Lord.

His answer wasn't the one we wanted to hear. How easy it would be to go ahead with our good plans even if God hadn't given His stamp of approval. With anguished hearts we released our dreams. In years to come we would look back and see this as a crucial test – a choice that would impact our future and our usefulness.

Who would be there for Melissa if we adopted Adam? No, there are other fine Christian families who could give Adam a loving home. Melissa needs us. Still it is hard to let the dream go…

After our younger daughter was diagnosed with neurological problems—problems that might be genetic—Jim and I had decided not to have more children. Adopting another child, perhaps one with a handicap, had been a dream even before we met Melissa. Only God's "no" when we prayed stopped us from approaching her with the idea.

But God, surely it's not too much for her to ask for Christian parents for Adam. Look at the incredible sacrifice she has to make. She desperately wants him raised to know you as Lord and Savior.

"Why doesn't God just tell me what He wants me to do?" Melissa asked. "Why doesn't He let me in on His plans for Adam?"

"He doesn't usually send telegrams," I said reaching for my Bible, "but He puts some clear road signs in His word."

No stories about girls in Melissa's situation came to mind, so I began thumbing through the Old Testament hoping something helpful would leap out at me.

"Moses! His mother gave her infant son to Pharaoh's daughter in order to save his life. Pharaoh's daughter certainly wouldn't have been a Hebrew mother's first choice, but God had it all worked out for good. It was all part of God's plan to deliver His people from slavery and lead them to their own country," I assured her, as I continued flipping pages stopping next in the book of 1 Samuel. "Hannah. She waited so long for a son, and then gave him to the priest Eli to fulfill divine destiny. Samuel grew up serving in the tabernacle not living at home." Melissa leaned in eager to hear more.

That morning we discovered that over and over the Bible described godly love as a giving love, not a grasping, hold-on-for-all-your-worth love. Finishing our skimming study of the Old Testament we moved on to the New. The gospels revealed the ultimate in God-like love—giving His son to rescue an undeserving world. From front to back the Bible told us that real love sacrifices, choosing the best for the one loved even in the face of pain and ridicule.

Several days passed while Melissa absorbed this new knowledge. Quiet but not so depressed, she moved through the daily routine…

"She's crying again," Grandpa sighed, easing himself into his favorite chair. His leathery hands move in a restless rhythm up and down his thighs. "What should we do?"

"There's not much we can do. This is a really tough decision, and she's afraid of making a mistake. I'll look in on her later," I reached over to squeeze his hand, "Pray, Grandpa."

After watching the news, I'd go see what I could do. But for a few minutes I would focus on the world's problems rather than the ones in my home. When a silly comedy replaced the news I turned to Grandpa. "I'll see how Melissa is doing." Feet dragging I headed toward the stairs. This is so hard. What do I say? What will really help her?

"Jim and the girls should be back anytime now," I called over my shoulder. I'm so glad he took them out for a McDonald's™ supper. Shelly gets so upset when Melissa cries.

Just as I reached Melissa's door, she opened it, "I called Julie this afternoon and told her to bring the papers around in the morning. I have decided to give Adam the gift of a family." There was a new calmness in her voice; this time I heard her heart as well as her head.

Quickly gathering her into my arms, rubbing her back, I asked, "Are you sure?"

She nodded, stepped out of my hug and smiled apologetically. "I guess I've known all along what is best for Adam. The problem has been with me. I wasn't sure I could let him go; I love him so much. But loving him means giving him the very best I can. Thank you for helping me see what God has been telling me all this time."

Signing the papers released a fresh flood of tears; for several days she was inconsolable as she mourned the loss of her son. He's gone as surely and completely as if he had died, and she needs time to grieve. These tears I can handle, Lord. It was the indecision and frustration that was so wearing on us all.

When I sensed she was ready to emerge from her cocoon of grief, I encouraged her to join The Family get-togethers again. Gradually she responded to my prodding, first sitting on the very edge of the group and simply listening, then quietly joining in, and finally her joy and enthusiasm began resurfacing.

With recovery, however, came the day we had all been dreading. The day Melissa decided to move on with her life. "I've decided to go home, to try to rebuild my relationship with Mom," she told us.

"Will you come back?" Holly wanted to know.

"At this point, I don't know." Melissa's smile trembled at the corners, "I left home too soon, before I was ready to be on my own. I want to go back, try again, earn a little money for school, and then decide about coming back to D.C. I think I might like to be a social worker like Julie Howe."

"Well, Minnie Mouse, you'd better keep in touch," Jim warned her, "'cause we're all going to miss you like crazy."

In less than a week Melissa was gone, leaving a hole in each of our hearts.

To help us work through our pain and loss, we threw ourselves into The Family's needs. We were committed to having more than a superficial relationship with them and that meant availability—not just a once a week meeting. The girls especially seemed to need "hang around time"—talking, sharing, being noticed. How they all vied for Jim's attention, squealing in mock protest when he ruffled their hair or giggling when he enfolded them in one of his huge bear hugs. It wasn't long until we had a steady stream of young people coming to our home at all hours…

But something is still missing.

"Sure is empty around here without Melissa," Grandpa grumbled.

"No classical piano, no assistant joker, no frilly doilies," Jim concurred.

"Well, why not place an ad for a live-in teenager," I joked. Chuckling, together we agreed it was a bad idea.

"But I bet we'd find a lot of takers," Jim muttered. "There seem to be a lot of unhappy kids around. Maybe what we should do is advertise for a home that can take in more than one girl at a time. I'd like to be a dad in a place like that. We do seem to have this crazy addiction to teenagers."

"What a great idea!" The more I thought about his suggestion, the more excited I became. "Maybe there's a Christian ministry somewhere that works with troubled teenaged girls—you know runaways and girls like Melissa whose parents have turned their backs on them."

We soon moved beyond thinking about houseparenting to searching for a ministry that needed us. The closest thing we could find was a Christian rehabilitation center for drug-addicted boys. Although not what we had in mind, we sent for the information and application. Who knows what the Lord has in mind? This might be just what He wants.

Neither Jim nor I would ever have guessed just what the Lord had in store.

Postscript

Melissa did go back to school, first for a degree in art. She has worked in the music field as a historic researcher. She allowed God to work in her unplanned pregnancy and bring her into a loving relationship with Himself. To this day she lives guilt free and without regrets for the choices she made for Adam and herself. On several occasions she has shared her testimony.

Although she had serious relationships and several proposals, she didn't marry until she was in her thirties. Adam remains her one child. We stay in contact, Melissa at times sharing her gifts and talent with us through poems and pictures.

Don't let me be ashamed
Of anything I did before,
You took everything away
And left only opaque memories,
Faded feelings, scraps of worn anguish,
And thrills that cheated my heart of peace.
Take them away,
So far away I can't quite remember…
Make them so unlike my new self
That my yesterday life
Is more like a book I read
Days and weeks and ages ago.

> --Melissa, 1977 (Six years after giving birth to Adam)

To think about

- Grieving is not always an indication that something is wrong—it may be a measure of how great our love is.

- Are you prepared to help another through a difficult time even if it means feeling their pain and not running from it?

- The best of parenting occurs in the best and worst of life's situations—when we laugh with our children or celebrate their success and when we walk with them through times of pain. It is then that we teach them endurance, patience and God's unconditional love.

- We all yearn to know a father's loving heart and strong arms. When they are missing our growth is stunted, our understanding of God warped, and our self-esteem damaged. Do you need to ask God to be the Father for your fatherless heart?

"You are the God who performs miracles;
you display your power among the peoples."

Psalm 77:14

Chapter Four

A Year of Miracles

"Just a couple more hours and we'll be official. We'll have done it," I said watching the lush Pennsylvania farmland roll by my window. Even after months of preparation and anticipation, I marveled at what God was doing. "The House of His Creation," I let the words roll around inside the car. What a perfect name for a home only You could bring into being!

"Well, the shell at least. We still need some girls." Jim teased.

"But it won't be long! Just think how much God has done already—Ron Lucas putting on a new roof for free—remember what Ron said when I told him we needed help in Pennsylvania, not Maryland?"

"Yeah. He said, 'Fine. The Lord put it on my heart to call you and where you use me is between you and Him.'"

"…the kitchen is fixed up—ovens, dishwasher, refrigerator—all given, selling our house for just the right price…" my litany continued.

"It's exciting watching as God moves on our behalf and wondering what He will do next."

Jim and I walked into the signing grinning from ear to ear. God was so good. ..and surprising. When our search for a home for troubled girls didn't produce any possibilities, we began talking about our dream of houseparenting wherever we went, to whomever we met—to family, to church family, at youth conferences—somewhere someone must know of such a ministry. It had to be out there, we just had to find the right person, the one who knew about it.

One of the men we talked to was Jim Brown, pastor of the Upper Octorara Presbyterian Church in Parkesburg, Pennsylvania. Although a hundred miles stretched between our home and his church, we and The Family had traversed it many times. The powerful Saturday night prayer and praise services were worth every hour of travel. God, in His creative way, had used bus trouble on our first visit to form a deep, lasting friendship. With nowhere to go and no way to get there (our only transportation sat groaning and wheezing in their parking lot), we and twenty members of The Family needed a place to sleep. Jim and his wife Ruth, along with several other members, had opened their homes to us.

We kept returning for the friendship and the fellowship, but mostly because of the tremendous blessing of Saturdays at Upper Octorara Presbyterian Church.

It wasn't enough to taste God's goodness; we wanted our church to feast as well, so we invited Jim Brown to visit. Sitting around our dining room table before the meeting, Jim Brown asked, "What's the Lord doing in your lives?"

"God's really put a desire in our hearts to see someone open a home with Christian foundations just for teenage girls," I replied.

"Maybe God is calling you two to start that home," he responded.

Laughing we shook our heads. "Help, yes. Start, no."

"Why not?"

"Well, for one thing, no qualifications," I answered.

"And for two things, no finances," Jim boomed.

"God has different ideas of qualifications than we do. You have the vision and the heart and an ability to relate to teens. And He certainly has no lack of resources," Pastor Brown pressed on despite our resistance.

"We wouldn't know where to start…how to build it," I insisted.

"Pray. Don't just toss the idea out because it looks impossible," he urged. "Find out what God's will is." What he said next really surprised us: "We can run the money for your home through our church until you get your own non-profit established."

Later when we were alone, we tried to reason away the idea of starting a home, but we admired and respected Pastor Brown too much to ignore his counsel. His final comments echoed in our hearts for weeks to come, "If the Lord is calling you into this work, He'll open the right doors for you to walk through. Just ask Him to show you the way."

Unexpected things happened—a phone call telling us about the perfect farmhouse for "our home" for girls, people volunteering to help, support from our home church, and ninety-year-old Grandpa telling me, "Anne, if God's telling you to start this home, then pack my bags! I'm ready to go!"

And so the search for a house was underway before we even realized it. We prayed, we asked for counsel, we prayed some more. We looked at properties. We talked about what a move to Pennsylvania would mean.

At last, sure that God was telling us to step out in faith, and finding a property we could afford, we sealed the deal with a Christian "handshake." The owner was adamant that, "Papers aren't necessary between Christians." Besides, he was a member of our fledgling board. So months before signing the agreement to sell, we began repairing the house. Twenty to twenty-five of The

Family came every weekend to help, counting the work of their hands and their time as their personal gift to Jesus. The van rides to and from Pennsylvania rang with laughter and praise—we were in the middle of a great God-adventure with miracles appearing like signposts along the way.

So, late one afternoon in May we arrived at the signing, eager to establish the Lord's home for girls. Glancing around the owner's home we searched for our lawyer but didn't see him. He must be running late. In fact, the owner's lawyer is missing as well. This may take longer than I thought. Not too long, I hope. Jim has to be at work tomorrow morning. Walking into his living room, we discovered two of our advisory board members were there. Why are they here? Jim and I are buying the house not the ministry.

Our next clue that all was not going as we had thought was the look on the owner's face as he approached us—tight smile and eyes that made darting passes at us but never really made contact.

"Mr. and Mrs. Pierson…"

What happened to "Jim and Anne?"
"There's been a change in plans. I found out that a developer wouldn't be interested in the farm land around the house you were looking at…"

Looking at, we've just about finished the major repairs.
"He'd be afraid the value will drop when people know there is a home for troubled teens right in the middle…"

"We're not taking in felons!"

"I'm sorry, but I can't sell you the house," he concluded.

"But we had an agreement."

"Nothing legal—in writing. Sorry, have to protect my investment." Taking a quick breath he continued, "Here's what I'd like you to do. Rent the farm house…"

"Renting won't lower the property value?"

"I'll reimburse you $200 for the repairs you've made."

Lord, we've invested thousands of dollars of other people's money into that house. Father, this man is on our board! How can he do this to us?

We stared at the scattered pieces of our dream, as he remained adamant about not selling. Our world, like an out-of-control elevator, plummeted—pain and disaster swallowed us.

Gripping the steering wheel, Jim stared at the white lines while I cried the whole way back to Maryland. Lord, what went wrong? Did we miss You? What are we going to do? Our home is sold—we're supposed to be out in two weeks! But deep down, below the hurt and fear, ran a subterranean river of Jesus-peace. It kept us from shattering into as many fragments as our plans.

As the numbness began to wear off, we knew there was something we had to do, even though it could cost us every cent of equity and appreciation we had gained while owning our house. Jim and I contacted every person who had given toward repairs in the house. We did our best to explain the situation and offered to return all that they had given.

Everyone refused to take us up on our offer. In more or less the same words they said, "We gave it for a reason—for a home for girls. We still believe it will happen. God hasn't changed His mind."

When the buyers of our house couldn't give us an extension, we were faced with one of three choices—find an apartment in D.C. in less than two weeks, move to Baltimore close to the trucking company Jim worked for, or believe that God still wanted us to start the home and move to Pennsylvania in anticipation of His provision. Rather than try to figure it out with our heads, we decided to fast and pray for a week. We wanted to make sure we were doing what God wanted.

We listened to tapes, we searched the scriptures, and we asked for advice. On our knees in the living room with my mother praying up a storm beside us, we asked for answers—and we asked for love.

"Jesus, please heal all our wounds from this experience. Heal us so completely that even the scars are removed. And when we pass the owners in the street or at church, don't let us see what they did. Only let us see You working in this situation."

With less than a week until we had to be out of our home, an offer came from Leonard and Yvonne March, members of Jim Brown's congregation. "It isn't much—just a basement. But if you need a place to stay, you're welcome to it."

It was the confirmation we needed. Even so, it was hard to take that final step. Moving day came, and we stood around chatting with The Family and sipping coffee. Only when the buyers' arrival was imminent did we begin carrying boxes and furniture to the trucks. When everything was loaded, ninety-year-old Grandpa climbed into the U-haul™, and we headed for Pennsylvania driving toward a future hidden in God's hand. When I had gone to Grandpa's room to tell him of our decision to move, he cocked his head and looked me in the eye. "Are you sure it's God?"

I nodded my head. "Well, then pack my bags, I'm ready to go."

I guess we're never too old to follow YOU on a new adventure! We wrestled with doubts—had we really heard God calling us to this ministry? Was it just our own idea? Why had God allowed us to put so much time, effort and money into renovating a home that we would never own?

Each day Jim would make the two-hour drive to his job in Maryland while I searched for a place to live. One day I found a mobile home that fit our budget, but I couldn't find a lot to set it on. The next day I located a lot, but when I returned to buy the mobile home, it had been sold. I never expected to find my desert experience in a basement.

Finally in desperation, I returned to a large farmhouse we had looked at as a potential home for girls. Bigger than the one we had agreed to buy and then lost, it was currently divided into five apartments—maybe one was vacant.

"We wondered how long it would take until you came back," the bed-bound owner said as soon as I walked in. Just that quick we went from apartment hunting to house buying.

Their huge old farmhouse was just what we were looking for— except for the price. But even more than its size making it right were the ten years of prayers saturating it. The elderly couple who owned it had been asking the Lord to have a ministry for troubled teenage girls buy their property. Now that the wife was terminally ill with cancer, they really wanted to sell. First they reduced their asking price, then they accepted a second mortgage to help with the financing.

In spite of the fact that the amount left was still more than we could afford, we approached the bank. After sharing our plans and admitting we could not prove that we would make the payments, the bank loaned us the money.

In July of 1972, we moved into the House of His Creation—a name we found in 1 Chronicles 4:31, the name of a town Beth Biri which means the House of My Creation.

Our only steady income was Jim's job as a trucker, not nearly enough to make the $500 mortgage payment along with all the other

monthly bills. God used surprising ways to meet our needs, mostly
the generous giving of people who believed in what we were trying to do. Local farmers brought produce from their gardens and
fresh meat as well. Total strangers mailed us checks with a simple
explanation "for the Lord's work."

As fast as tenants moved out of apartments we began renovations, converting them back into bedrooms. And as fast as we
were creating bedrooms, the Lord was filling them. Jim and I had
registered as foster parents with several child-welfare agencies in the
tri-county area. Our first girl, a runaway, had come to us just three
weeks after we moved in. Five months later there were fourteen
girls sharing our home. With another bedroom just about ready,
we would soon welcome four more...

The phone in my "office" (actually a corner of the living room)
rang. "House of His Creation, Anne Pierson speaking," I tucked
the phone between my cheek and shoulder so I could continue
opening the mail piled on my desk.

"Anne, this is Eleanor Graham over at Chester County Children's Services. I'm looking for a place for one of my teenagers
who is pregnant. Do you have room?"

Pushing the mail to one side, I reached for pen and paper. A
pregnant teen!

"Yes, I believe we can make a spot available," I hoped my voice
sounded more calm and professional than I felt. Of all the girls
we accepted—school truants, rebels, and the abused—the ones
that excited me most were the pregnant ones. Already we had two
living with us. If this one came as well, we'd have three deliveries
to anticipate in the months ahead.

"Her name is Allison. She's fifteen...due date's April 20th,"
Miss Graham continued.

"I can't guarantee Allison admission. She must choose to live with us—it's policy."

"Not a problem. Allison has a very difficult home situation. I'm sure she will be pleased to live with you folks."

After setting the date for the pre-placement interview and hanging up, I stared out our living room window. Fifteen, the youngest yet. First a seventeen-year-old, then two sixteen-year-olds. Is this a trend? Lord, please let Allison come to us with an open heart and mind. And please give Jim and me all the love and patience she'll need.

A "rat-a-tat-tat" on the door punctuated the end of my prayer. "I'm home," Melissa poked her head around the door. "I'm going to run some errands in town. Need anything?"

"No, thanks, hon, but check with Aunt May," I smiled as she vanished as quickly as she had come. Melissa's re-entry into our lives had delighted us all. Things had not worked out with her mother as she had hoped. "Can I live with you? If I can find work in Pennsylvania, I'll be able to pay for room and board this time. I can help with the housework and cooking too."
Even our vivid descriptions of all the repairs that needed to be made did not discourage her. And so Melissa became part of our extended family again. When she wasn't working in the offices of the local school district, she helped around the House and acted as big sister to all the girls.

Melissa was one of three special assistants God had sent who were essential to the smooth and successful running of our house. The second was Cindy Harris, a registered nurse and good friend from our church in Maryland who had moved to Pennsylvania with us. Although she taught full-time at a local nursing school, she lived at the House, filling the roles of counselor and heading our "department of health."

Our third helper, the incredible Aunt May, had offered her services before we even purchased the House, "I'll watch your children, cook your meals, scrub the floors… You name it, I'll do it!" Cheerfully giving up her home to work alongside us; she was truly a godsend. "The Lord has put it in my heart to help you in whatever way I am needed. Just tell me what you want done." Her sincere, no-strings-attached offer was a gift straight from God's hand.

This widow, who had already raised four sons, leaned into the immense tasks facing us with the energy of someone half her age. Sleeping on a mattress on the floor like the rest of us, creating tasty meals out of whatever food was available, painting, scrubbing, mopping—she tackled every job with enthusiasm and humor.

But most importantly she wrapped us all in prayer—Jim and I, Holly, Shelly, Grandpa, Melissa and Cindy, and all our "girls"— everyone, everyday was covered in prayer. She didn't stop there either, her prayers reached out to include our garden, animals, even the paint and plaster. Like one of her delicious stews, the House of His Creation simmered in her constant prayers.

I would have been completely overwhelmed by this amazing and diverse household of twenty-two (twenty-three if Allison came) without Melissa, Cindy, and Aunt May. Jim was still commuting two hours a day to his job in Baltimore, and when he was home, all his time was spent on the renovations.

Truly this was a house of His creation—no human being in their right mind would have assembled such a large, diverse group in an old house needing so much work.

Postscript

After months of negotiations and waiting, the owner of the first house we were going to buy sent us a check for $200 as reimbursement for the time and materials we had invested in his house. Since Coatesville is a small town, we met them frequently in stores and at church. The Lord was providing us with many opportunities to exercise love and forgiveness. Like all exercise programs, it was difficult but the results were worth all the effort invested.

To think about

- Miracles happen to those who need one—are you willing to be placed in such a situation?

- God gives you a vision and a plan. He usually expects you to do the work.

- Between getting a vision and seeing it fulfilled, there is usually a desert. You must be willing to walk through the desert and let it work character and integrity into you.

- Wonderful relationships come in all ages. You can learn valuable lessons from both the young and the old.

- Bitterness would have short-circuited God's plans. Learning to let the pain and disillusionment go is absolutely necessary if we want to be useful in God's kingdom. Are there wounds you have never allowed to heal? Are you tempted to be angry at the owners who reneged on their deal with us? Don't. The price is too high!

"…for God's gifts and his call
are irrevocable."

Romans 11:29

Chapter 5

Allison

The tall, extremely thin teenager shivered in her unlined jacket. Frayed cuffs that reached the top of her wrists and a broken zipper told of hand-me-downs and poverty. In a hurry to get Allison out of the penetrating November wind, I opened the front door even wider. "Come in out of the cold."

Miss Graham began the introductions, "Anne, this is Allison Barnes. Allison, Mrs. Pierson is the lady I've been telling you about." I doubt Allison saw my smile since she was staring at the floor in sullen silence. Frizzy black hair cut in an Afro ringed a mahogany-skinned face. She glanced my way for an instant then focused on the floor again. I was dismissed as totally unimportant. This one isn't ready for a hug or even a handshake, Lord.

"Please make yourself comfortable, Allison." I pointed to an easy chair in my office. Feet shuffling in tennis shoes one size too big, she crossed the room. She surveyed the area without interest, her expression motionless.

Miss Graham handed me a summary of Allison's file—several typewritten pages thick. If it takes this many sheets to summarize it, how fat must the actual file be! This girl is no newcomer to Social Services.

With no time to read it, I held it in my lap where I could sneak peaks at it. Looking up, I smiled at Allison. "Where do you go to school?"

"Coatesville High." Legs carelessly crossed at the ankles, tailbone buried in the cushion, back curved—Allison obviously wasn't excited to be here.

"What's your favorite subject?'

Her shoulders twitched—a shrug in miniature. "Dunno."

"What do you like to do with your friends?"

"Hang out." Every word a cold monotone.

All right, Anne. This isn't working. She doesn't want to talk and you aren't going to make her. So you talk instead.

"Let me tell you about The House of His Creation. We have fourteen girls living with us right now. Anywhere from ages thirteen to twenty. A couple are pregnant like you. Most are having problems at home."

Pausing, I checked for signs of interest. Nothing.

"My husband and I set the rules. We all share in the chores—and the fun." Glancing at the papers in my lap, several phrases caught my attention… "welfare family"… "school problems"… "neglect." She's barricaded herself against anymore pain.

When I looked at Allison again, I saw the defensive hunch of her shoulders. Eyes down, face blank but with a slight tilt to her head. She was listening.

"We have lights out at eleven, and everyone eats breakfast together at eight thirty."

No response.

"There is a school for pregnant teens in Coatesville. Two hours a day in a church basement." Allison stirred and sat a tiny bit straighter. Finally. Come on, Allison, talk.

I glanced at Miss Graham. She shook her head, opened her mouth, then closed it again without saying a word.

I plunged back into my monologue. "We also require you to complete one Bible study each week and to go to church with us every Sunday morning." She'll head for the door any time now. She doesn't look like a girl who likes rules.

"No one can make you live with us unless you want to. But if you come, you must obey the rules."

For the first time her eyes connected with mine briefly before she looked away again. "I know. It's okay, I'll come."

Uh-oh, I wasn't expecting this. Can we really help her? She probably figures we're the best out of a bunch of bad choices.

"Take a couple of days to think about your decision. Make sure this is the right place for you," I encouraged her. Her stare, which had been boring a hole in my wall, swiveled back in my direction. No uncertainty, no hope either. She's not going to change her mind. She's ours until her baby comes—if we take her. Should we?

While walking them to the door, Miss Graham finally spoke, "Thank you for holding a place for Allison." Her smile apologized for the ordeal this interview had been. "A new case worker will be assigned to Allison once she is living with you."

I must have looked alarmed for she quickly added, "It's the policy of my agency. All girls are reclassified when they become pregnant."

Turning to Allison, I tried once last time, "It was nice meeting you."

Nothing.

"We'll wait to hear from you."

No response.

Is she going to remain silent for the next seven months? She either has nothing to say or thinks I'm not worth talking to.

After watching the car pull out of the driveway, I hurried back to my office and Allison's history. As I read the summary, her behavior began to make sense. Her home life was a disaster. Food and shelter were in short supply; love, encouragement, and hope were nonexistent. Her father had no means of support—except for the monthly Aid to Dependant Children checks. To ensure continued resources, he encouraged his daughters' boyfriends to sleep over. This resulted in pregnancies and more and bigger government checks. A man with a gambling problem, he confiscated all the checks coming into the home to feed his habit.

Older sisters also lived at home with their own infants. There seemed to be no exact head count of those living in the house. However, the only income came from monthly welfare checks. In other words, Allison's baby would give her new status—her own welfare card and monthly child support to pass along to her father.

So much for my talk about normal family living. I might as well have been speaking Portuguese. She has no concept of a normal family life.

Faced with Allison's cold silence, I had hoped she would refuse to come. When I began to understand how dismal her life must be, compassion pushed aside my urge to reject her. She needed so much, and we would have her for such a short period of time.

Is it possible to have a lasting impact? There is so little we can do—a temporary home and medical care. What will her future be? Lord, help us find some way to help this child of Yours. Give us ways to show her how unique and special You made her. Let her see Your plans for her. Give us Your patience and love in the weeks ahead. Thank You for this opportunity to serve You as we welcome Allison into our family.

I had to repeat that prayer many times in the next month as despair and hopelessness made repeated attempts to slither back into my heart.

Allison moved in two weeks after our first meeting. Clutching two brown paper bags, which held her entire wardrobe and all her personal possessions, she once again stood shivering on our front porch. Deciding to ignore her silence, I welcomed her to the House of His Creation and introduced her to Jody, her new roommate. Warm and caring, young and pregnant, Jody was chosen by Jim and Melissa as the girl most likely to make Allison feel welcome and at ease.

Jody's chatter and bubbly laughter drifted down from the bedroom they shared. It wasn't long before two pairs of footsteps were heard climbing the wooden stairs to the attic. Jody had taken one horrified look at Allison's clothes and hustled her off to our used-but-nice boutique housed under the west end rafters. A warm coat, sweaters, maternity slacks, and a bathrobe were piled into Allison's willing arms—no longer needed by someone else, but treasures to a girl used to more ragged hand-me-downs.

Although still quiet, Allison did not stare through Jody as if she were a windowpane. In fact on one of my trips upstairs, I heard Allison respond to a question with three complete sentences, a miraculous string of twenty words without sullen pauses.

When Aunt May sang out the call "supper's ready" and we all converged on the dining room table, Allison was careful to choose a chair that was neither beside nor across from an adult. Oblique glances out of the corner of her eye monitored our locations—she was careful never to get too close.

At least she's got Jody. That's a start.

Allison continued this awkward dance—retreat when we came near, side step shuffle to avoid contact—for a week. "We can't let her continue to ignore us," I said at staff meeting.

"I'm not sure that's what she's really doing," Melissa said. "I think she's scared. Not angry or bored, frightened."

"Why would she be afraid of us?"

"Remember her reaction to Jim?"

Before supper that first day, Jim had moved forward to meet our newest girl: A semi rumbling towards a VW Beetle. Automatically his arm had wrapped around her shoulders for a welcoming squeeze. Whites gleaming around her eyes, she had twisted away and backpedaled until she bumped into a wall. Not just timidity at Jim's size. Out and out terror.

Now that I knew what to look for, it was plain to see. When Jim was in the room Allison glued her eyes to him, darting to the left or hustling through the door to stay away from him.

On the other hand, I would have been delighted for just a tiny bit of the respect she gave Jim. I was an annoyance—a state-paid drill sergeant…

The new duty roster had been distributed at breakfast. "I shouldn't do this kind of work in my condition," she said. "Let someone who isn't pregnant clean the bathroom."

"Everyone takes turns. Your baby will be just fine."

With loud sighs of exasperation and dramatic eye-rolling, Allison suffered through Aunt May's demonstration of the proper cleaning techniques. In a suspiciously short amount of time she declared the job was done.

Gray rings clung undisturbed to the sides of the tub and sink.

"Did you have trouble with your chore, Allison?" I struggled to keep my voice calm and pleasant.

"No!" was her only verbal response but if she had had feathers, every one of them would have been ruffled.

"Well, we need the tub and sink scrubbed with cleanser to get rid of the ring."

"I already did that. They must have come in and messed it up again." "They" being any of the girls except Jody and herself.

"Please try again."

"That's not fair!" A stream of loud, colorful protests and excuses followed, seeking a crack in my resolve—a way to erode my determination and get herself off the hook.

Don't give in. Stay calm and pleasant. "Please clean the sink and tub."

Slamming the door, she returned to the grimy sink. Again I checked her work. Still gray and grimy. I sent her back to try again...the ring remained. Finally after the third try, the room passed inspection. Allison retreated, grumbling, to her room.

Chores weren't the only battle zone. Mornings required "artillery" and the occasional "rocket" as well to get Allison up and moving. It was almost impossible to send her off to classes on time. Weary of confrontations, I put Jody in charge of morning maneuvers.

Whether it was setting the table, making her bed or sweeping the floor, Allison's response was always the same. First she complained; then she whined. When those tactics didn't make me throw up my hands in surrender and allow her to skip her chores, she would drag the job out endlessly until I wanted to grab the silverware, sheets, or broom and finish the job myself. Don't do it, Anne. That's exactly what she wants you to do. You'll lose not only the battle but the war as well.

The only time I got cooperation—forget cheerful—was when Jim was around. Thumping the trash cans like they were kettle-drums one Saturday morning, she collected the garbage in stony silence, tossing looks of disgust in my direction. Moving into the kitchen to gather bags there, she met Jody.

"Hey, you said you'd never take out the garbage. What happened?" Jody stopped washing dishes to stare.

"Her old man is home. If he ever hit me, I'd be dead," Allison yanked the bag out with enough force to set it swaying.

"Jim? Why worry about him? I've never seen him hit anybody. Not even look like he wants to. He's big, but not mean," Jody chuckled.

"Yeah, well, I ain't takin' chances. He comes in, I go out."

Later, I told Jim what Allison had said.

"That does it!" he said, slapping his knee for emphasis. "Starting this weekend, I'm making Allison my number one assistant. It's time we got to know each other."

How I looked forward to Saturday morning! Most of the girls adored Jim, considering it an honor to be chosen as his helper no matter what the task, but I was sure Allison's response would be very different. For once I could watch the battle of wills from the sidelines instead of as one of the combatants.

Breakfast finished, Jim pushed back from the table and said, "Okay, Allison, get some old clothes on." Grinning his most innocent grin, he pulled back her chair and helped her up. "We're changing the oil in the tractor."

Wide-eyed Allison stood perfectly still. "But I…I can't…" she stammered. Her glance bounced around the kitchen as she looked for an escape. "I mean, I don't know othing' about tractors."

"Well, then it's time you learned," Jim said, turning her in the direction of the stairs and giving her a little nudge. "Get dressed and meet me in the barn in ten minutes. No dawdling." Jim's smile never wavered as he talked, but no one doubted he meant exactly what he said.

A grease-splattered Allison returned to wash up for lunch. As usual she didn't participate in the lunch chatter, but a small tinge of red slipped over her cheeks when Jim said, "This is the best mechanic in the bunch." And a tiny grin appeared when he added, "Never saw any girl learn to handle the old tractor so quickly."

"Hey, Allison, grab your coat. We're going to the store," Jim directed the following Saturday. She studied Jim's face a moment before heading for the coat closet. No enthusiasm yet, but no resistance either. Progress at last!

Less than an hour later, Allison ran into the house, doors crashing behind her, and tears streaming down her face. She disappeared into her room with a violent slam of the bedroom door that set the china dog rocking on the coffee table and sent our cat Malachi hissing to the top of the bookshelves.

"I know exactly how you feel," I soothed the irritated cat. Take a couple of deep breaths, Anne. Teens are dramatic. Then find out what's wrong.

Just then Jim walked into the room. It can't be too serious—he'd be moving faster.

"What's wrong with Allison?"

"She's okay. Why's Malachi perched up there like a vulture?"

"Allison slammed one too many doors on her way through the house. She didn't act 'okay.'"

"While we were at the store, I asked her if she wanted an ice cream bar." He stopped to clear his throat and blow his nose. "I don't think she's ever had her own ice cream treat before. Her eyes lit up like I'd offered a trip to Disney."

"That still doesn't tell me why she's so upset."

"Well, the ice cream was melting a little by the time we reached the turn-off. A big chunk of chocolate fell on her coat. I don't know if the tears are for the lost ice cream or for the stain on her coat," Jim said with a chuckle. "Either way it's no catastrophe. I told her the stain would come out, but she kept on bawling."

"All those tears over a chunk of ice cream?"

"Yup."

I double-checked Jim's face to make sure this wasn't one of his jokes. He's serious.

"I'll go reassure her."

I returned defeated fifteen minutes later. Even though she had allowed me to mop up her tears and gently rub her back, she didn't stop crying nor would she tell me why she was so upset. I'll check with Jody later. Find out why Allison overreacted so ...

"She said she'd never owned a new coat before," Jody shrugged. "She's afraid you'll get mad and take the coat back."

"Oh, Jody! I hope you told her we would never do anything like that."

"Well, sure. But she didn't believe me this time any more than she's believed me the other times I've said it," Jody shook her head. "I don't think she trusts you guys very much."

True. She doesn't trust us. She's afraid to let her guard down—we might disappoint or hurt her. She keeps looking for a "catch." She doesn't recognize loving acceptance—yet.

But Allison's heart was softening even though we couldn't see it. In just a few weeks it would be visible, but by then another problem was forcing its way into the center of my attention.

Severe stomach pains put me in the hospital for an extended rest and a complete work-up. A lot of multi-syllable medical terms were tossed around—something to do with my blood sugar—but there was one diagnosis I recognized without a dictionary: "exhaustion." Too little sleep and too much stress had my body sending SOS signals via my stomach.

"You can't be constantly available to a bunch of troubled teens without repercussions. The strain is too much," Dr. Alexander lectured me. "Either share the work load or allow The House of His Creation to destroy you."

I knew he was right, but I had no idea how to share the load. Our Board of Directors had one very emphatic idea. Jim.

"God called you both to this work," Pastor Brown said. "Don't worry about providing a paycheck, Jim. It's your presence that is needed." The board put Jim on full time status just as quickly as he was released from his current job and gave us a joint salary of a hundred dollars a week—payable as funds were available and after all other expenses were covered. "The Lord has provided for this ministry all along. He won't forget you now," Jim Brown insisted.

With those four hundred dollars a month we had to cover our insurance, medical bills and clothing for our family as well as our long distance phone bills. Because of Holly and Shelly's health problems, the loss of Jim's salary—and his health benefits—was another incredibly huge step of faith for us. Once again we had to be absolutely sure of God's call and be able to rest in His provision.

So in January 1974, Jim began spending all his time at The House of His Creation. What a tremendous change in all our lives—especially mine! With his knack for handling touchy situations and disciplinary problems, our home became the haven it was meant to be. I was freed to focus my energies on the care and counseling that required a mother's touch. Our marriage took on whole new dimensions as well as we learned to appreciate and rely on each other's strengths. The household flourished and so did my health.

Only because the House of His Creation was truly God's call to both of us did we make all the adaptations and adjustments necessary when you live, work, eat, and sleep with your marriage partner. It was truly a "twenty-four/seven" arrangement. I had to give up chauffeuring the girls to their appointments, something I loved, but I also joyfully gave up the very early morning wake-up calls to Jim who is a morning person. All the adjustments, even the good ones, needed the lubrication of grace and the cushioning which comes from flexibility.

Word of our adventure with God was spreading, reaching beyond the local community. Speaking opportunities at churches and civic organizations began to open up across the state and even further away.

At first it was to small groups of women meeting in church basements—five to ten who listened and then returned home to tell their husbands. Together they would share what they had heard with the church body.

God touched hearts as we talked and gifts to the ministry increased. This made it possible to pay the bills and our one hundred-dollar a week salary. The money flowed not in a steady stream, but in bursts and trickles. It seemed we were always in financial crisis without ever falling into a full-fledged catastrophe.

Daily we thanked God for the provision He would supply for the ministry, and daily we brought our family's financial needs to Him as well. Some days it was so hard to trust Him. At times it was also very tiring.

I found myself anxiously waiting for the mail to arrive. Would there be money for the bills? Any left over to continue the needed remodeling? Would the money for the mortgage ever come before we faced the deadline?

Daily He provided—as we needed and not before.

He also provided referrals through those speaking contacts— soon we had girls housed in every conceivable space, and almost half of them were pregnant.

To think about

- Want to experience God's compassion? Open your heart and eyes to those who have less than you do.

- God reaches into each of our hearts in unique and custom-designed ways. We should expect nothing less from the God who created individual fingerprints. So don't expect God to touch and direct someone else in exactly the same way He touched you.

- Find and nurture your marriage partner's unique, God-given strengths if you want to accomplish great things for the Lord.

- Some are called to a lifestyle of faith for personal provision. Others are called to be God's instrument of provision. Which is your calling? Either call obeyed yields the same reward—an increased knowledge of God and a life of blessing others.

"Out of his fullness we have all
received grace in place of grace already given."
John 1:16

Chapter 6

Legal Troubles

Babies don't consult anyone's calendar when choosing their time of arrival—unless of course it is to deliberately pick the most crowded day or least convenient hour, which is just what Allison's baby did.

A few determined rays of sunshine poked through the overcast sky, bringing a hint of spring and welcome relief from the past two weeks of cold, gray weather. Although frosty, March 22nd was starting out well.

The breakfast table rang with laughter and teasing.

"Here, Jimmy, you need another pancake."

"Aunt May, I'm taking you home with me to teach my mother how to cook."

Jim Brown's phone call added to our high spirits. A new septic system estimated at $5000 had been a prayer project for weeks without any sign of God's answer. With ever increasing urgency, board members, staff, and girls had asked the Lord for the money we needed. Although unglamorous, the system was an absolute necessity. Now an anonymous donor had volunteered to pay this very large bill.

Joining hands around the table we ended our meal with rejoicing, "Thank You, God, for meeting our need. Bless the person who has given so generously. Amen."

Then it was time to scatter—Aunt May to supervise the laundry, Jim to the barn, Melissa and the pregnant girls to school, and me to my office where stacks of paperwork demanded my attention.

A few minutes later Melissa poked her head around the door saying, "Allison isn't feeling well. I don't think its anything to worry about. Her due date isn't for four weeks yet, but she is cramping. You don't mind if she missed classes this once, do you?"

A few months ago I would have been highly suspicious, but that was before she had decided to trust us.

Since then Allison had accepted her responsibilities with grace, if not outright delight. Still sloppy and undisciplined in her personal habits, she was making an all-out effort to be a dependable member of the family. This new Allison would not use sickness as an excuse to get out of school.

"That's fine. I'll check on her in a few minutes."

A quick glance at her watch and Melissa hurried down the hall. "See you later," drifted back over her shoulder. My paperwork, however important, would have to wait a little longer.

"Hey, how are you doing?" I sat down on the side of Allison's bed.

"Okay, I guess. Just tired. Didn't get much sleep because my stomach hurts."

I smoothed her hair back from her forehead and smiled. "Stay in bed and relax. I'll come see how you're doing in an hour or so."

"You're not mad at me for missing class, are you?"

"Of course not. You're our star pupil these days. It won't hurt to miss one day."

Allison grinned and patted my hand. "You're okay. I always knew we'd be friends after we figured each other out."

What a wonderful day this is, Lord. Needs met. Lives changed. It doesn't get any better than this. I didn't realize how quickly it would change…

The phone was ringing as I returned to my office.

"Is this the House of His Creation?" a brusque male voice demanded.

"Yes, it is." There obviously isn't time for pleasantries in his life.

"Do you take in teenage girls?" was the next question fired at me.

"Yes, we do, but…" I was ready to tell him we were filled to capacity.

"Well, you can't do that!" the man shouted in my ear.

"Excuse me?" I stammered, rattled by his belligerence as much as by his words. "What do you mean we can't—we're registered as foster parents with the proper agencies…Who are you?"

"Albert Martin, Pennsylvania Department of Health and Human Services," the words still coming at me like bullets. "How many girls do you have right now?"

I didn't have to stop and count. Just two days ago, we'd accepted another pregnant teen, bringing our count to an all-time high of seventeen. We were back to borrowing cots.

"Seventeen!" the man echoed. "As foster parents you're limited to six minors at any one time. You are seriously at odds with the laws of the Commonwealth. Just how many of these seventeen are under twenty-one?"

"All of them." Courage, Anne. Don't roll over and play dead. "No one ever told us there was a limit on the number and so many agencies seem to be desperate for homes…" Tears burned my eyelids and panic swelled in my chest.

But Mr. Martin wasn't finished. "Ignorance is no excuse. The Commonwealth has regulations and minimum standards to safeguard the minors in its care..." The litany went on and on. I tried to write down the important points, but he spoke so rapidly and I was so upset that I really didn't catch much of what he was saying. One point, however, was clear—we could look forward to inspections by several state agencies in the very near future.

"And," he concluded, "try to get rid of some of those girls!"

By this time tears pooled on my desk, smearing ink and wrinkling papers. What are we going to do? All this work to be shut down. What if there are fines?

Finally I remembered I didn't have to bear this alone – Jim was here somewhere. I just had to find him.

He was teaching Blossom, our new calf, the fine art of drinking from a pail, his big hand gently scratching behind the knobby top of her head as he crooned encouragement.

I barged into their conversation—I needed Jim's soothing more than Blossom. "Jim, I just had the most awful phone call." The words spilled from my mouth, tripping over each other on their way to his ears. "He thinks we're doing something wrong. He said he could close us down in twenty-four hours if he thinks it's necessary! The inspectors will be here within the week."

Jim gathered me close for a hug; then planted a kiss on the top of my head. "Let's back up and start over. Who called? What inspections?"

I repeated my tale of woe—this time a little slower and a little more coherently.

"As far as shutting us down, I wouldn't worry," Jim said. "Once they see what we're doing they'll calm down. Don't forget, this place belongs to God and nobody puts Him out of business."

Stepping back, I returned his smile with one of my own, although mine did not equal his in either size or steadiness—it wobbled in the middle and faded at the corners.

We spent the rest of the morning on the phone asking board members to attend an emergency meeting that night. Next I briefed Aunt May; her prayers are more powerful than official regulations.

What happened to my wonderful day? Noon and not one bit of paperwork finished. How will I ever get caught up?

I stared at the piles on my desk—correspondence with supporters, medical reports, and a week's supply of Bible studies all needed to be done now.

Bible studies first. They won't impress state authorities, but there's nothing more important to our girls' futures. It helps them discover who they are. And they need the chance to know the God who loves them. They all feel so unworthy, even unlovable. So hungry for self-worth and purpose. Just last week Amy, one of our troubled teens, had discovered God's forgiveness through these studies. With all the headlong enthusiasm her age is known for, she had grabbed that forgiveness and healing for herself, and now her eyes shone with life, and her smile started in her heart and spread to her face.

Of course not all the girls became Christians while in our home, but we planted seeds of love and hope in every life. The harvest was God's responsibility, not ours. He could easily cause our seeds to grow even after years of lying dormant. Besides seed planting, the Bible studies helped me monitor each girl's emotional and spiritual health and provided the insights I needed to counsel effectively.

Allison's study was near the top. A big smiley face beamed at me from her paper. Look at this Mr. Martin. Looks like "well-being" to me. A poem in Allison's far-from-perfect handwriting was scribbled next to the face:

"Roses are red, violets are blue,

I'm glad I came here, I hope you're glad too."

I had asked the question "What do you think of God?" Allison's answer was honest and ambivalent, "I think maybe God is real and maybe He loves me. I'd like to get to know Him better and be able to trust Him but I don't think I can."

She's never known a human father's love. Never seen any evidence that she has personal worth. It's so hard to accept God's love without those affirmations. Still, there is hope. She wants to know Him.

I wrote on her paper: "You are indeed loved by God. He has wonderful plans for you, if you follow Him. And, by the way, I think you're pretty neat too!"

Allison wasn't feeling any better by dinnertime. Concerned, I asked Cindy if we should take her to see Dr. Rowghani, our obstetrician. "I really don't know what to make of this pain. It's early for her to be in labor, and she doesn't seem to be getting any better."

"I'll run her over to his office," Cindy volunteered.

Wonderful. one crisis down and one to go. Now to organize the facts for tonight's board meting.

But before I could marshal a single piece of information...

"Anne, you'd better come," Melissa didn't even wait to enter the room, but sent her voice on ahead. "I think Allison's water just broke." She stopped to catch her breath. "She wants to see you. She's really scared."

It didn't take long for Cindy to confirm Melissa's suspicions. Practice had made us experts at packing: throw bathrobe, slippers, and nightie into a suitcase. Toss in toothpaste, toothbrush, shampoo and hairbrush. Grab layette set and coming home outfit for Mom. In less than five minutes I had bundled Allison into the car and headed for the hospital.

"You start the board meeting," I told Jim. "If Allison's not ready to deliver, I'll try to get back for at least part of it."

Dr. Rowghani met us at the hospital. He said, "This could be a long night. She's leaking amniotic fluid, but hasn't dilated very far yet. Can you stay with her?"

The board meeting... It will just have to go on without me. "Sure, I'll be right here."

Here we go again. At least it no longer terrifies me. Nine months in the House and six deliveries later, I'm practically a pro! Not the scared rookie I was the first time when Joan went into labor...

Less than a month after we had opened the House, Joan and I made the trip to the maternity ward. The labor waiting room with its institutional gray-green walls and year- old magazines had done nothing to soothe the nervous flipping in my stomach. This was an alien world despite my own two deliveries, for I had been out cold during both of them and remembered precious little. A maternity nurse had appeared with a reassuring smile, "We're prepping Joan now, Mrs. Pierson. In just a few minutes you can go in and be with her. She's apt to be awhile, since this is her first baby."

Oh, can't I just stay out here, Father? I'm not going to be any help in there! I waited for His reassurance. His silence was a rebuke and I surrendered. Well, at least I hope someone's around to tell me where to go and what to do.

The nurse popped into the room, interrupting my fretful thoughts, to announce, "Things are really hopping around here." Her voice breathless as she held a shapeless green gown by the shoulder seams while I fumbled with sleeve openings.

Tossing a shower cap-like thing at me, she continued, "I hope you don't mind being alone. We have two women who will deliver any minute, and I don't have anyone to stay with Joan." Next came giant sized cloth booties. Swathed from head to toe, I looked like a reluctant caterpillar peering from its cocoon.

Before I could explain my total unsuitability as a nurse's assistant, she was half-herding, half-shoving me through the door into the room. Each step tightened the tangle of knots in my stomach.

It was too late to retreat—Joan had already spotted me, calling out a cheery, "Hi, Anne. I was afraid you'd deserted me."

The smile on my face was as tight as the muscles in my stomach. Walking to her side and taking her hand in mine I glibly replied, "Wouldn't miss it for anything."

Mimicking a model's turn at the end of the runway, I pivoted, arms in exaggerated pose, "Don't you love the high-fashion designs they wear around here?"

At first it wasn't too bad; Joan and I giggled and talked as if we were sitting at the kitchen table sipping cups of tea. Only brief timeouts for Joan's contractions, now about five minutes apart, interrupted our chatter.

But that changed when Joan stopped talking in the middle of a sentence, arched her back, and turned to me with wide, panicked eyes. Her forehead glistened with perspiration while her face flushed a muted shade of red. Releasing her breath in a big sigh, she whispered, "I'm awfully glad you're here, Anne. This is a lot scarier than I thought."

She doesn't have to tell me how scary it is. Where's that nurse?

It seemed that Joan had barely relaxed before she was squeezed by another super-contraction. Sweat popped from her forehead and rolled into her eyes. Blinking away the sting, she turned to me for reassurance and comfort. I had none to give. When the third wave of pain shuddered through her, I reached for the call button dangling by her pillow.

Somebody—anybody but me—has to be here when she delivers. I ought to know more about this.

No bustling, competent professional appeared...an eternity passed, along with three more seismic contractions, before a nurse ran into the room, checked under the sheets, and hurried out again. Another eternity, crammed into a couple of minutes, passed before an aide entered with a gurney, "Hop over here, honey. We've got to get you to the delivery room."

Finally! That means you-know-who is off duty. Prepared to pace the floor in the traditional manner, I retraced my steps toward the waiting room only to be stopped short of my goal. The nurse who had hurried me into Joan's room was beckoning from the delivery room doors. "You'll have to stay with her a little longer. We'll be just a few more minutes over here," gesturing to another brightly lit delivery room. "She'll be okay. Just keep her distracted, and for heaven's sake, don't let her push!"

Joan's cry of pain was the only thing that kept me from running after the nurse as she vanished behind a pair of swinging doors.

Okay, you can't let Joan see how scared you are. Concentrate on her needs not your discomfort. And start praying!

I might have thought whole eternities had passed before, but I was wrong. Eons crept by in the next twenty minutes as I begged over and over, "Please, God, don't let this baby arrive before there is someone here who knows what they are doing." A male nurse appeared and announced he was only a student. Standing at Joan's feet holding a towel, he looked like a receiver ready to catch a football. Not a reassuring sight, Lord. And neither are all these metal contraptions.

The glittering equipment, tucked away in every corner, was a silent witness enticing my imagination to follow paths I really didn't want to explore. Suddenly, noise and activity replaced the hushed atmosphere as a doctor materialized and began scrubbing his hands and arms—the brush a blur of motion racing over his fingers. The nurse dashed across the room hurling sterile sheets over Joan and ripping open packs of instruments.

Don't even think what they might be for, Anne!

A couple of steps back and I could no longer see their shiny, threatening shapes—besides I needed to step aside so that the professionals could take over.

"Stay where you are!" the nurse commanded. Surely she doesn't expect me to assist with the birth! Her tone softening slightly she added, "I'll put up a mirror so you and Joan can see the birth."

Mirror adjusted…doctor and nurse poised…and just in time, for with a great push, a small head with swirls of blonde hair emerged. Flailing arms and a slippery body followed rapidly—the wait was over; Joan's baby had arrived squalling in red-faced bewilderment.

Joan and I stared fascinated as the miraculous bundle of humanity wailed his displeasure. The doctor snipped the cord and made it official, "It's a boy."

Handing the wriggling, noisy little fellow to the outstretched, blanketed arms of the nurse, he chuckled, "Isn't it something? No other performance on earth comes close to the drama of the birthing show. Congratulations, Mom."

Joan, teary but smiling, looked at me and whispered, "Thanks for being here with me. I love you."

"I wouldn't have missed it for the world. I love you, too."

Soon the nurse had weighed, measured and cleaned the baby. She brought him over, "Here he is—all seven pounds, two ounces and twenty inches of him. What do you think?"

Nine months and six more deliveries later, the labor rooms were familiar territory.

The night shift's going to find me here again. They're sure to tease me about my girls' preference for nocturnal deliveries.

For several hours Allison experienced only mild contractions, which left plenty of time to talk.

"You know, I really didn't like the House at first."

"Hmm, I noticed," I winked. "Why didn't you?"

"I wanted to stay with my boyfriend. It makes me mad that Dad wants my government check but not the expenses of my pregnancy and the birth." Her hands clenched—and not because of a contraction, then relaxed.

"And then there was the problem of Jimmy." A huge grin replaced her scowl. "Remember how scared of him I used to be?"

"Scared? You were terrified! The look on your face when he told you to help change the oil in the tractor..." We laughed at the memory.

"I thought I would die," she said between chuckles.

"And you looked like it too!"

"Yeah, but I like him a lot now," she said shyly. "I love it when he introduces me to people as his daughter—just like I really was his kid. And not ashamed of me either. And opening doors and things for me like I'm a real lady. He's not scary at all once you get to know him."

"I think he's pretty neat, too," I casually wiped the two tears trickling down her nose. "That's why I married him."

A brief inspection by the nurse interrupted our conversation, but Allison went right back to her House review when the nurse left. "It sure was neat of Aunt May to teach me how to hook a rug. She never got upset when I made a mistake."

The rug in bold blues and greens, had been a source of pride and awe for Allison.

"Grandpa's so nice. Always cheerful." She paused and swallowed, "I'm sure gonna miss you guys when I have to go."

The day shift left and the night crew made their rounds. Allison's chatter had become more sporadic. "I'm gonna be a good mama," she said. "I'm gonna finish school and get a good job. Have me a nice home—you and Jimmy and your kids can come visit."

"It sounds wonderful, Allison."

She must have felt my concern. "Just you wait and see. I'm really gonna do it."

Maybe she will. But she's only fifteen—street-smart, but immature. Can she nurture a baby? Get a job? Public assistance is her only inheritance. It will be such a struggle to break free.

The night shift waved good-bye as the day shift took over. Ever increasing pain tightened Allison's hold on my hand, but she didn't cry out or ask for medication. Dr. Rowghani had explained that the medicine, which would ease her discomfort, could have a negative effect on a premature baby. So she suffered through the hours in silence. I was impressed.

Finally at eight am the baby appeared—thirteen hours after Allison had been admitted. Weighing five pounds, her little girl looked more like a doll than a real live infant, but to Allison she was perfect.

"A girl! Just what I wanted! I'm gonna name her Candace and call her Candy. She's gonna be my sweet little girl."

By the time I had fussed over Candy, escorted Allison back to her room, and called the good news to the House, it was nine o'clock. Nine. Twenty-six hours since I've slept. I trudged to the car for the drive home. Maybe a nap until noon. Paperwork still not done. Board meeting—wonder what they decided.

Jim and Aunt May met me at the back door. "Straight up to bed. No arguments!" they ordered. "We've got it covered. Go get caught up on your sleep. You'll be of no use until you do."

I was asleep before Jim had the covers tucked around my shoulders.

It was dark when I turned over and cautiously opened one eye. The clock by the bed announced nine o'clock. Twelve hours gone. How could I have wasted so much time? All the work…I tossed back the covers and reached for my clothes.

"No, you don't," Jim's voice came from the corner.

"But all the work…"

"Don't worry. We took care of everything while you snoozed. We have five new girls and two of them are expecting twins."

"Mr. Martin would have a fit," I laughed. "But the board meeting…"

"Later," Jim said holding a hand, palm out, like a traffic cop.

"Shelly thinks you're sick again, and Holly has some terrific news from school. The board report can wait."

Obediently munching left over potatoes and meatloaf, I listened as Jim told about Judy Markle's visit. Judy, passionate about Lancaster Birthright and persuasive at finding places for pregnant teens to live, always talked us into taking another girl.

"She wanted us to take another girl."

"Yep!" he was careful not to look at me.

"Jim! You didn't. With the state inspectors and our being way over their limit…"

He grinned and let me rant a little longer before he said, "I told her to see you tomorrow. Let's see you turn down the girl. Bet you can't do it."

"Bet I can. You didn't have Mr. Martin shouting in your ear." Besides, everyone knew that Jim was by far the softer touch. He would willingly pack every corner of the House with anyone who asked for help. In fact we limited the amount of cash he carried because the chances were good he'd give it all away. Judy may have convinced Jim we should take the new girl, but I knew how desperately we needed to lower our head count.

I'll explain. She'll understand. No more girls for awhile. Not until the legal mess is sorted out.

To think about

- Our relationship with our earthly father spills over onto our relationship with our heavenly Father. We need to spend time knowing God so that the 'spill' flows the other way.

- There are times when we need to care for others, but there are also times we need to accept care from others. Both giving and receiving need to be done with grace.

- Don't draw back from new experiences because they may highlight your weaknesses or ignorance. Childbirth and labor, a situation I tried to avoid, became a very great joy in my life—after God firmly walked me through my reluctance.

"May the Lord direct your hearts
into God's love and Christ's perseverance?"

2 Thessalonians 3:5

Chapter Seven

Inspection!

Crisp, freshly ironed curtains hung at the windows. Every dust bunny had been hunted down, trapped and hauled out. Sinks, tubs, and door handles sparkled. Step into the House of His Creation and the first scents to hit you were lemon and ammonia-clean.

Bring on the state inspectors. They've got to be impressed.

"Unless they're blind, they've got to see how special this place is!" I said to the group seated at the breakfast table

Their knock at the front door came at nine o'clock on the dot. The woman, small and hurried, carried a huge manual which she referred to repeatedly as "the regulations." The man measured rooms, consulted with the woman, examined our files, and occasionally pointed out one of our shortcomings in a gentle voice.

Each time they found another infraction she would flip pages in her regulations, "Tsk," and jot another note on her clipboard. He, with a slightly apologetic air would mention yet another deficiency. My records on each of the girls were deemed totally inadequate and incomplete, which wasn't surprising since they consisted of an index card listing the girl's parents or guardians and their address. Paperwork had not been a priority.

The relentless inspection dragged on and on. Without smiles or extraneous conversation, they moved through the house, barn, and grounds as unstoppable and efficient as a bulldozer. The man asked questions from time to time: How had we done this? Why did we do that? Perhaps it was the look in his eye, but I suspected he genuinely cared. The woman, however, was there simply to see that we complied with the regulations.

Four o'clock came—every square inch assessed, every file examined—and they issued their ultimatum: five girls must be told to leave that very day. "Before tomorrow morning you must have not more than twelve girls living here."

Lord, help! I need wisdom right now. Taking a deep breath and reminding myself that God's Word makes it plain that I must honor those in authority over me, I said, "All the girls are emotionally attached to us. If we chose five and tell them to leave, they will see it as rejection and a withdrawal of our love. And these girls don't need any more of that. Perhaps you should talk to the girls and choose the five you think should leave. And if you tell them they have to go and why, it won't hurt them so badly."

"That really isn't our responsibility," huffed the woman. At this point the man intervened urging her aside for a consultation. When they returned she said, "We will extend a grace period for you to achieve your required limit. As the girls leave, you may not replace them until your count is lower than twelve."

She handed me my very own copy of the intimidating manual she had clutched throughout the day and a very long, very detailed list of all our failings.

"You are not operating a foster home. This is a group home. You must re-apply for certification in that category," the woman informed me. Thank You, Lord, for Your grace and favor.

"Please note the other requirements listed on the inspection sheet. Many are urgent and need prompt remediation."

This will cost lots of money—which we don't have.

"The others can be done over time, but within a year. Otherwise you will be found delinquent on your next inspection as well."

Delinquent kids, delinquent house, almost delinquent payments...

"You will be inspected by the Departments of Labor and Industry and Health shortly. I'm sure there are fire and safety inadequacies as well."

Why not? The more the merrier.

The man turned to Jim and shook his hand.

At least he doesn't look like he enjoyed his day's work. That might almost be sympathy I see in his eyes.

She marched straight to the car; he got as far as the porch steps before turning to face us. In a voice so soft we had to strain to hear it he said, "I am a man of faith, but until today my faith was like grape juice. Today it became wine." The formidable sight of all the obstacles facing us kept me from realizing just what he had said. It would be days later before I could appreciate what God had done under my nose while I was too worried to notice.

I sagged against the front door, my arms filled with manuals, forms, and inspection sheets.

"We've had it. This is the end of the House."

Jim didn't argue or join my pity party. Instead he calmly pulled the inspection sheet from the pile I clutched and began reading it.

"Where are we going to get a full-time paid counselor? Or the money for a family room? And the kind of files we need!"

Jim pointed to one line on the sheet. "We can do this without any additional money, just some re-arranging."

"But what about all the rest of them?" I waved a handful of complaint forms in his face. "We'll never be able to comply with all of them."

The only realistic thing to do is give it up. It's time to quit.

"They've given us a whole year, Anne. A lot can happen."

He's right. I'm still scared and depressed, but he's right. I'm so glad he's a rock when I'm Silly Putty™.

"Has God ever failed us, Annie?" was Jim's parting question as he returned to the barn to finish the chores. How like him to give me a one-liner to chew on and then give me the space to do my "eating" in peace!

Jim waited patiently for my depression to lift—no false cheer, no urgings to "snap out of it," he just continued to do each day what needed to be done. I had just about climbed out of my "hole" a week later when we got back-to-back visits from the other two state departments. In a list almost as long as the first, they catalogued all that must be changed, modified, or eliminated. The attic had to be sealed off. There goes our storage area and where will we put our boutique? We must install fire doors on all stairwells. Our beautiful open stairway! A fire plan created and practiced which would meet state requirements. At least it doesn't require money.

My misery hole was beginning to feel too familiar and comfortable—and with these new lists—too inviting. Jim put these lists with the other one before going out to feed Blossom. Why can't I lay these problems down as easily as he does?

Life in the House had not been suspended during the weeks of inspections. It was like living in two separate universes simultaneously. Judy Markle had visited the day after Allison's delivery just as Jim had predicted; in fact she was waiting in my office when I returned after hospital visiting hours.

Her smile is like a heating pad for sore muscles. It's going to disappear when I tell her we can't take another girl. Wish I didn't have to.

"How about a cup of tea?" I asked. Nothing like putting off what you can't avoid.

Sipping hot liquid, I finally faced the problem, "Jim says you have another girl who needs a home and maternity care."

"That's right," Judy's hair bobbed with her enthusiasm. "This girl's unusual," she began.

I held up my hand. "Did Jim tell you that the state has told us to 'get rid' of some of our girls—that we have too many? We've decided not to take any new girls until we've been inspected and approved."

Judy's first reaction was surprise—Jim had obviously not mentioned our problem to her. After listening to my recital of Mr. Martin's phone call, she laughed bitterly. "Too bad you don't want to open an abortion clinic. There's a lot less concern about businesses like that than about homes that save lives."

I've never seen Judy so upset. "What are you saying?"

"If you wanted to go into the abortion business, all you'd need is a building, a doctor, and a cash register—that's all it takes," she choked the last words out. Impatiently brushing aside her tears she continued, "The trouble with the House of His Creation is that it aims to help girls who don't want to have an abortion. That kind of business requires close regulation by our government."

So shocked I could only stare, I let her fumble for a tissue until I realized a box was on the end table next to me. I handed her one, then grabbed her hand giving it a comforting squeeze. "They're not trying to make it difficult to help the girls. They just want to make sure we are doing right by them."

"I know," she sighed. "It just seems that the law is a little lopsided when it comes to providing a viable option to abortion. The girl I wanted you to accept is desperate to carry the baby to term, but she'll end up in some abortion clinic if her family and so-called friends have their way."

Knowing I was making a tactical error even as I said it, I asked for more information about the girl. "Just remember we must honor the state regulations if we want to be approved as a home for girls."

That was all the invitation Judy needed. Meredith Anderson was indeed a unique case. A twenty year-old student who was nearing the end of her junior year at nearby Franklin and Marshall College and came from a wealthy family didn't fit our usual profile.

"She transferred from the University of Pennsylvania just to be near her boyfriend. He's a senior. They plan to marry next spring when she graduates," Judy explained. "If she gets an abortion, that is. He's told her the wedding is off if she has this baby. He wants her to have an abortion and so does every other person who should have her best interests at heart."

Guess I've been pretty naïve about abortion. I know the Supreme Court said last year that a woman can have an abortion in the early months of pregnancy, but a normal, healthy couple doing it for convenience? Parents pushing it for the sake of family image…How can they treat life so lightly as if there is not another tiny person involved? And this is happening all over our nation? Poor Meredith—needing to stand against all those who should be standing with her. I just don't understand how they can do it. It's senseless.

"Doesn't Meredith have even one friend to help her? Give her a place to stay?" I asked. "If her family is wealthy, surely…"

"No one. She hasn't made any close friends because she was spending all her time with her boyfriend. Her family has told her no more financial support if she doesn't have an abortion. Her tuition and board are paid through the end of the semester in May. Then she has no one, no money, no place to live."

Someone has to help Meredith. Surely there is someone besides Jim and me.

"Her parents are 'loaded,' but short on love and forgiveness. She's worse off than our welfare mothers—no one wants to help the over-privileged," Judy concluded. "The whole thing makes me so angry!"

How do I say no?

"I suppose you could at least bring her over for an interview. Once she sees us and the House, she'll probably choose not to come. No luxuries and conveniences." And that would let us off the hook without a nagging worry—wondering if we should have tried to help. "She'll be older, more sophisticated, than our girls." She'll see that she doesn't fit in. "But we can show her that some people support her decision not to abort. How is she standing so strong without any encouragement?"

"She had an abortion when she was younger—it was already legal in New York. She won't discuss it. Gets very upset if I ask her questions about it. It must have been really traumatic."

"It's hard for me to imagine…"

"Anyway you needed to know that to help her."

"Wait a minute. I didn't say we would take her."

"But you will meet her."

"Yes. She won't be interested though." Didn't you say the same thing about Allison? But this is different. Meredith is different. She can't be interested. How in the world would I explain to Mr. Martin that we'd added to the household instead of getting rid of a few?

The state inspections with their staggering lists had pushed aside thoughts of Meredith so when Judy's call came two weeks later to set up an interview, it was a bit of a jolt. Now more than ever, we were in no position to accept new girls. Reluctantly, I agreed to a meeting.

Meredith arrived dressed as if she were applying for a position with IBM—expensive tailored suit, gold wristwatch, Gucci bag and coordinated accessories. Her pleasant smile and agreeable attitude never faltered even when I described, in graphic detail, the chores all the girls were expected to do.

Come on, Anne, can you see her on her knees scrubbing toilets?

I went through all the rules and regulations for the House.

A twenty-year-old will resent these.

I waited for her to realize this wouldn't work, but she continued to smile and nod in all the right places.

"Do you have any questions for me?"

Without hesitation, or taking time to think, she asked, "May I move in on May 15th? That's the last day we can stay in the dorms." For the first time I saw her falter. "I…I don't have anywhere to go after that." Her voice trailed off and her eyes focused on something not in the room. She's reduced to begging for a place to live. How bewildered she must feel.

I looked at her, this time seeing beyond the clothes and accessories that shouted money. She's as needy as any of the welfare girls we've accepted…You're afraid. Afraid you won't earn her respect because of her wealthy background and college experience. All your objections have been attempts to protect yourself.

Realizing the less-than-Christ-like workings of my own heart had me squirming in my chair. It stripped away my reasons for refusing Meredith a place in the family. Still my concern was valid—would Meredith be able to adapt to our simple lifestyle with its limited conveniences? How will she fit in with the other girls? Isolation and loneliness would be doubly painful after her parents' rejection. But it was her choice.

"All right, Meredith, take a week to think it over and if you still want to join our family give me a call." Surely six will be gone by May fifteenth.

One girl we had expected to leave very shortly after the inspection was Allison. Her father would certainly be eager to get Allison, Candy, and their check in his control. But Candy's premature birth increased concerns about her care, especially since Allison's home provided substandard conditions: drafts from ill-fitting windows and doors, ancient flooring which was the home to legions of germs and bacteria, and an overall disregard for cleanliness. The social workers were reluctant to release Allison and Candy into that home environment.

We had made a policy not to take any mother and child into our home after delivery, which meant Allison was with us, but Candy was in foster care. We knew it was best for the ministry and for the other girls, although it was very difficult for Allison.

Some girls put off making any plans for their future. If we welcomed girls and their babies into the House, we would be encouraging that problem. By placing the babies in foster care, the young mothers had the time and opportunity to discover if they were prepared to parent. This separation pierced the romantic bubble surrounding their babies and allowed the reality of their situation to come into focus. Sometimes the bond between mother and baby grew stronger, and the mother became determined to find a way to raise her child.

If we bypassed this critical process we created unstable single-parent homes where the baby bore the brunt of this decision.

Many of the children removed from their homes because of abuse would never have been put in these perilous environments if the teen mothers had had a period of time to discover for themselves whether they really had the maturity and determination to parent. We needed to tell those young women, "It's okay if you can't parent right now. In five years you may be a great mother."

Allison's social worker was taking a hard look at Candy's care and trying to find alternative housing for Allison and her baby. Allison's age and educational requirements were compounding the problem—who would care for the tiny newborn while Allison was in school?

All of this meant Allison's options were very limited. Finally the various social agencies came down to only one solution. Send Allison back to her father's home. First they would try to educate her father and other family members to provide the safest environment they could for Candy. It certainly wasn't ideal, but it was possible. The father's gambling problem and obvious welfare fraud were ignored.

"I wish someone would start a home for young mothers and their babies," I vented my frustrations to Jim one evening. "They need a support system, help with parenting techniques, and built-in childcare while they finish school or train for a job. They'd have responsibilities just like the girls do here—ways to earn the right to stay, but… "

"Stop right there," Jim warned. "The last time we said 'somebody ought to…' we turned out to be the 'somebody.' We can't handle any more ministries."

I chuckled at Jim's mock horror. "I know we can't, but someone else ought to. I'm really concerned about these young girls trying to parent." It was so easy to see where they and their babies would end up without help—the welfare rolls, a place of poverty and little hope.

There was one thing I could do, if I could squeeze it into my schedule: take the Childbirth Education Association's (CEA) classes. Then I would be able to teach our girls prenatal care and prepare them for delivery. I would be able to slip in some parenting skills as well.

I applied for the program even though I didn't think I had much of a chance of being accepted. To my surprise my lack of experience didn't disqualify me. This is one ambitious program, Anne. Can you do it? Eight weeks of classroom theory. Four weeks of hands on. Three months of crowded schedules, not to mention carving out study time...Lord, I really need your wisdom for this one.

Finally I made my decision: I had to try.

May fifteenth. Meredith was coming but first we had to see Allison on her way. It had taken so much longer than anyone expected for Allison to be given permission to return home.
Candy, now a plump cutie, arrived at the House at ten am—she certainly didn't look like the preemie I'd first held in the hospital. Allison tucked tiny arms into a new pink dress while we all cooed and fussed over her. Next came the matching bonnet and sweater— all gifts from the staff and family at The House. Candy's exuberant arm waving made Allison's awkward dressing even more difficult. Will Candy thrive in Allison's care? So much responsibility...so little preparation. Life will be so hard for the teen and her little girl. Jim had found urgent business in the pasture this morning; he preferred to cry in private. He had said "good-bye" yesterday over a final ice cream treat. How he hates sending his girls out into an uncertain world! Fortunately all the girls understand Jim's soft heart and his need for private good-byes.

"Well," Allison turned to me with a smile that trembled. "I guess we're ready. Tell Anne goodbye, Candy. Tell her to come see us."

I grabbed them both in a last hug. So hard to let them go. They need care and protection. "I love you both very much. You keep in touch. Call anytime."

Then with more hugs and a lot more tears, Allison, aged fifteen and a half, left with Candy, aged two months, to start life as a family.

Dear Lord, please break that cycle of poverty and hopelessness. Don't let the sins of others hold them in bondage. Let them live the beautiful lives You designed for them. Let Allison's dream of a house and dignity and a job come true.

Postscript

For a while it seemed that she would beat the odds and live her dream. She completed high school and was accepted at a local business school. State-provided vouchers paid for Candy's childcare while she trained.

Then one day, without notice, her childcare provider stopped accepting the vouchers. This left Allison with no one to care for Candy. Discouraged, Allison withdrew from school. She didn't have the resilience and hope that a good self-image and family support would have given her.

Her loneliness drew her into another dead-end relationship which soon resulted in a second pregnancy. She and her children were trapped in the welfare system. As a good mother with high standards for her children, she realized they would face an uphill battle.

Because of the welfare reform act, Allison eventually returned to school to train as a dental hygienist and invited us to her graduation ceremony. Rushing to greet us, it was obvious Allison still valued our support and love. Our biggest challenge continues to be knowing when and in what form God wants that support to take.

Allison has found a job and is once again moving toward her dream.

We don't know if she is looking to God for help. We do know that good seeds of the Gospel message were planted during her stay with us. They can sprout even after years of lying dormant and appearing to be dead. Fortunately we are not responsible for the harvest; God only asks that we plant seeds of love.

To think about

- Providing unconditional love has a far greater impact than providing material things.

- When you reach out to meet one need, you will always see many others. The secret is to ask the Lord which ones you are to meet.

- "For I know the plans I have for you," declares the Lord, "plans to prosper you and not to harm you, plans to give you hope and a future." Jeremiah. 29:11

- We will either be a part of His plans or be putting up roadblocks keeping others from His plans.

- What appears to be disastrous may actually be God's opportunity to demonstrate grace and power. Keep your eyes on Him and off the circumstances.

"Trust in him at all times, you people;
pour out your hearts to him, for God is our refuge."

Psalm 62:8

Chapter 8

Meredith

Images of Allison, Candy in one arm and a shopping bag of clothes in the other, climbing into the social worker's car kept reappearing in my head. Hoping some strenuous physical labor would make those pictures fade, I joined Aunt May and Cindy upstairs where a massive re-arranging was in progress.

We wanted to settle Robin and Kate in their new room before Meredith joined them. Although these girls did not have Meredith's educational background, at ages eighteen and nineteen, they did have job experiences that made them more mature than our high school girls. It was the best mix we could devise—hopefully Meredith wouldn't feel too awkward with her new roommates.

Both Robin and Kate had joined the House months before and would be with us for a while yet—as runaways unable to return to their homes, they would need our help for at least six more months. Meredith's background is so different. Finding a comfortable niche in this family won't be easy. It may even be impossible. Worrying about Meredith replaced worrying about Allison: same emotion, I just substituted a different girl.

Judy and Meredith arrived shortly after lunch and almost immediately gave me something new to worry about as they pulled a set of four matched suitcases from the trunk of Judy's car. There is not enough closet space in the entire house for that many clothes!

"Meredith, why don't you unpack a few of your most comfortable, loose-fitting outfits? You'll need maternity clothes soon. The rest of your things can go into storage."

She agreed with a smile and went upstairs to check out her new room. Still I was uneasy. "I don't know, Judy. She's going to feel out of place here. If only her family would support her."

"She might surprise you," Judy said. "You're giving her a chance—the rest is up to her."

I watched for signs of trouble—and found none. Meredith's pleasant, undemanding attitude with her roommates allayed my fears. She was polite to the staff and did all her assigned chores with meticulous care and without grumbling. She's either happy or a very good actress. Then just as I began to relax, it started.

Kate thumped into her chair muttering about "the nerve of some people ordering me around like a servant." Since I always try to give the girls time and space to work things out, I went to "yellow alert": watch and wait for further developments.

I upgraded the status to "red alert" a couple of days later when Robin exploded, "She called me a slob! Just because I left my toothpaste on the dresser." Eyes snapping she vented, "Who does she think she is? Visiting royalty?" It was time Meredith and I talked. But she beat me to it…

"Anne, I don't like to complain," she said, "but someone ought to do something about the unhygienic conditions in our bathroom."

"Such as…" I probed.

"There's toothpaste splatter on the mirror. Someone left a strand of their hair in the sink. It's just not acceptable."

"They'll be cleaned again tomorrow," I reminded her.

"What about today?"

"Meredith, we're never going to meet House Beautiful standards for tidiness. We just have too many teenagers living here to achieve that."

"It's more than not tidy. It's a basic sanitary standard."

"Hairbrushes and toothpaste lying around is a matter of tidiness. Your home is very different from theirs. Your desire for neatness and order is unusual. Most teenage girls just are not that concerned about it."

"They should be."

"Please try to give the girls some slack...learn to tolerate their standards."

Her response was to grimace and stalk off.

The situation worsened. Although superficially polite and compliant with the staff, she was openly disdainful of the other girls. They retaliated with sarcasm and mockery. Meal times gave them endless opportunities:

"Please pass the salt."

"Yes, ma'am, delighted to serve you, ma'am."

With tightened lips Meredith ignored everyone at the table, eating with her left hand resting in her lap, as any etiquette book teaches, always careful to take dainty mouthfuls.

Supper finished, Meredith would retreat to her room to read a book. She shunned evening activities—game playing, TV watching, and jigsaw puzzles could not entice her to join us. She only tolerated us when she had to.

"Meredith, what do you believe about God?" I asked one day.

"I don't need religion. It's pretty silly." Boredom and condescension laced her words. "But I'll go to church if you say I must."

Her Bible studies reflected that same attitude—hurried and superficial answers—of bare toleration. Meredith was marking time.

Jim gave Meredith the nickname Morning Glory. While most of the girls prized an affectionate pet name from Jim, Meredith barely acknowledged him when he used that nickname. Then came the morning when Jim not only called her Morning Glory but gently ruffled her hair as well...

Without a word, Meredith jumped up and ran to her room to re-comb her hair.

"Oh, don't you dare touch my hair!" squealed Kate in a high and snobbish voice. "I just had it done and now you've messed it all up!"

"I'm sorry I messed your hair, Meredith," Jim said as soon as she returned. Her only response was icy silence for the rest of the meal. Jim felt terrible and the girls increased their mockery. How much longer will she put up with this? She is so unhappy. No mail from her family. One short visit from her boyfriend...of course, she had told him not to come. She probably finds her housing embarrassing. Maybe she's looking for a way out...

"Get me out of here! Take me home before I catch some awful disease," Meredith shouted at Mary, our new social worker. One glance around the clinic was all she needed to know this was not a place she wanted to be.

"I can't leave all the others here to run you home," Mary reasoned.

"I can't stay in this awful place," Meredith waved her hand at the scene in front of her. As usual the waiting room at the Prenatal Clinic of the Coatesville Hospital was crowded. Women, including our girls, who had no way of paying for their medical care and had received medical assistance cards from the state, could get free prenatal care here. No refined society matrons sat here, chatting about fashions and charities. No plush chairs and glossy magazines, just stark walls, females in cheap smock dresses and shrill voices.

"How long until our appointment?" Meredith scanned the room, probably looking for a receptionist.

"We don't have appointments," Mary broke the news softly.

"No?! Then why did we come?" Meredith sputtered.

"It's first come, first served. We take a number and wait."

"How long?" Meredith whispered, her eyes glazing over.

"All afternoon."

Meredith closed her eyes in weary defeat until the woman seated next to her stood up to be weighed…and almost fainted in Meredith's lap.

"Get me out of here!" Hysteria made her voice loud and sharp.

"I'm sorry Meredith, I can't. We must stay," Mary replied.

Like a crab crawling into its shell, Meredith withdrew into the least accessible corner of the room and watched in bitter silence, punctuated by outbursts when an unwashed woman got too close.

Mary finished describing Meredith's encounter with the Prenatal Clinic: "So she just became more and more agitated—almost hysterical. I'm sure she's upstairs packing her bags right now. Nothing I said seemed to help."

I gave Mary, "Thanks for dealing with it. You're such a blessing." And such a wonderful miracle of provision, Lord. Mary had left a well-paying, secure position as a social worker in a nearby hospital to become our full-time caseworker. She had given up benefits and taken a huge cut in pay to obey God's prompting.

Lord, how do I help Meredith? What can I say?

When there was no response to my knock, I opened her door part way, "May I come in?"

She had been sitting on the bed weeping. At my arrival she jumped up and began piling clothes on the bed. "I'm sorry," she sobbed, "I thought I could do this, but I can't! I'm never going back to that place again. It's not working out. I have to leave."

Sitting down on her bed and clearing a spot beside me, I urged her to talk. "I know you're very upset, but there's no need to rush around like this. Take a couple of deep breaths." I continued, "If you want to leave, you can, but I need to know your plans...Where are you going? How are you going to get the prenatal care you and your baby need?"

Reddened eyes wide with fear, she stared at me. Shaking her head in despair and defeat, she said, "I have no plans. No one in the whole world cares about what happens to me, so it doesn't make any difference where I go."

"It makes a big difference to me," I said patting the bed beside me. "Come, sit down. This is not the way to handle a problem, and you have a big one to deal with."

For the next hour she sobbed out her pain and frustrations. "My parents won't write or call, let alone provide any money. I'm so poor I have to take charity. And all the time my trust money is sitting in a bank making more money."

"I thought you got a letter from home just a couple of days ago. Maybe your family is softening."

"Not likely," Meredith laughed bitterly. "The note was from Candice, my older sister. They expect me to come running home—as soon as I come to my senses and do the 'smart thing' about this pregnancy." Meredith plucked the corner of her pillow before continuing. "She said I'm being stubborn and stupid. She'd never let an unplanned pregnancy ruin her life."

"That really hurts, doesn't it?"

"She's 'Miss Perfect Daughter' who always does everything right. A lot she knows about mistakes." Suddenly crumpling against my shoulder, she cried, "What am I going to do? I can't stay here. I can't go home. I've made such a mess of things."

Giving her a reassuring hug, I let her pour out all her anger. "I'm sorry," she said after venting for another fifteen minutes. "I know I'm behaving badly, after you have been so nice to me. It's not that I'm not grateful, it's just..."

"This isn't the way you hoped things would work out. I understand. But you're forgetting one thing. You can stay here. You do have a way of meeting your medical expenses. Isn't it worth the inconveniences and the difficulties of the Prenatal Clinic to know you have someone looking after you? It's a trade-off—some unpleasantness in exchange for security."

She sighed, "I guess so. It won't be easy...How often do we have to go to the clinic?"

Later, discussing the situation with Aunt May and Jim, it suddenly occurred to me that Meredith needed some positive strokes. "Maybe give her an area of responsibility. It would make her feel more a part of the House and recognize her maturity."

"How about the storage shed?" Jim said. "It sure needs sorting and organizing. All that donated food is a jumbled mess right now."

"Let's try it. She could do a super job of putting it in order. We'll make her the official manager of the storage shed."

"And I'll put her at the top of my prayer list," promised Aunt May. "Poor little girl. What's the matter with her parents anyway?"

"I'm sure they think they're doing what is best, but they must have twisted priorities. And Meredith's paying the price. Please do pray—she needs God's comfort."

Prayer and positive experiences – what an incredibly powerful combination.

To think about

- God does not make us accountable for the outcome, only responsible to do what He commands. Trust Him to take care of the results.

- God sometimes uses overwhelming situations to move us toward wholeness and healing.

- Learning to see things through no matter how difficult is one of the great challenges in life and yet the rewards are beyond measure.

" in God I trust and am not afraid.
What can man do to me? "

Psalm 56:11

Chapter Nine

Troubling Confessions

Meredith and I stood knee-deep in boxes admiring the orderly rows of canned food lining the shelves of the old shed. "If we follow the system Jim and I set up, we'll always use the oldest supplies first," she said, swiping an arm across her forehead and leaving a dust trial behind.

"This is wonderful! I'm impressed." Thank you, Lord, for this idea. This has been so good for her. I suspect her favorite part is giving orders even the staff must follow. But she's doing a great job.

"Hey, Morning Glory! Where are you?" Jim's voice boomed from the back porch. Making a path through the remaining boxes took time and before we reached the door, Jim poked his head in. "Come out here, Morning Glory. You've got a visitor."

A mix of pleasure and embarrassment spread across her face. What a time for Greg to visit. She's sweaty and dusty. He could have called first.

When we first stepped into the bright sunshine all we could see were two dark shapes, one much larger than the other. It took several seconds for our eyes to adjust. It wasn't Meredith's boyfriend standing next to Jim but a man dressed in an expensive three-piece suit.

"Dad! What are you doing here?" Color ran up Meredith's cheeks, her smile coming and going, unsure but hopeful.

"I was in the area on business," Mr. Andrews said without a smile. "I thought I'd stop in and see how things are going." If he were any stiffer, he'd have rigor mortis. His pin striped suit looked out of place in our ragged farmyard. He feels as out of place as his suit looks.

"I'm fine, Daddy," Meredith said in a cautious whisper. She tried to stretch her smile wider, "Everything is okay."

"Good, good," Mr. Andrews said and swallowed. "Uh, I thought maybe…that is Mr. Pierson says there are a few decent restaurants in town. I wondered if you'd like to go to lunch with me."

Now she had no trouble smiling. "May I go, Anne?"

"Certainly. Take as long as you want." Finally, her family is showing some interest. She is so pleased. She needs them so much. Meredith hurried to her room to change into her nicest maternity outfit.

Jim and I watched them pull out of the driveway in Mr. Andrews's late model Mercedes. "He seems a decent sort," Jim said, "Afraid to admit how much he cares about his daughter—but a nice guy."

"If he would just bring his wife along next time," I said, building dreams of happy reconciliation.

"Don't count on it," Jim cautioned. "He doesn't even dare tell her he stopped in today. Apparently she's seeing this pregnancy as a blot on her motherhood."

"At least he came. She's so sad and lonely…I wish Greg would be more supportive." That would be a huge miracle, Lord. He seems so cool and calculating. Nothing that interferes with his master plan will be tolerated—including his own child. What he wants has to come first…I know I've prayed, but I guess I don't really expect him to change. And his visits depress her so…

In fact after his last visit, Meredith had admitted that she wished he would stop coming. The more her pregnancy showed, the cooler he became.

Meredith's father didn't stop with that one visit. He dropped in to see her several times over the next four weeks. And he almost always found a reason to spend time with Jim questioning him about The House, our funding, and his daughter.

"He can't figure us out," Jim reported. "Why would anyone open their home to girls they didn't know?"

Meredith's reaction to our House had been like her father's. When she moved in we were in the middle of a big construction project—adding a family room onto the rear of the house. Since the project depended completely on gifts of time and money, it was in our daily prayers. And when our prayers were answered, we rejoiced together at the supper table.

"Why don't you have a fund-raiser? That's what Dad's lodge does when it wants to do a community project." Meredith asked. "How are people supposed to know what you need if you only pray?"

"God has always supplied what we need," I explained. "He wants us to trust in Him, not in people."

Meredith shook her head in disbelief. We obviously don't have an educated approach to life. Faith certainly isn't a part of her world. But as the gifts came in, one by one, she began to catch the excitement of living expectantly. Her face would light up when Jim announced a special offering. She's not ready for faith yet, but she's certainly enjoying ours.

"Maybe Mr. Andrews is asking all those questions because he wants to contribute," I suggested to Jim after one of his visits. I bet it will be a big gift too.

"Afraid not. He promised his wife not to give one penny towards Meredith's support. Until she changes her mind, don't expect any money from him," Jim's smile was rueful. "And according to Mr. Andrews, that will be a long time coming."

The next break in the Andrews family front came a few weeks later. Meredith's kid brother, who was in training at UCLA for their swim team, began writing regularly. Unlike her older sister's note, his letters made her laugh. A family thaw had definitely set in—and a major warming trend was on its way. Finally the day arrived when Meredith received a letter from her mother.

Later that evening she came looking for me, letter in hand. "May I ask you something, Anne? Or am I interrupting?" While studying for my fetal development test was important, making time for questions was more important. I laid my open textbook down on my lap and smiled.

"I'm glad for a break. What's up?"

"My mother wants to know what I plan to do about the baby. I don't know what I'm going to do," Meredith's voice rose at the end, catching the attention of the girls who were putting together a giant jig-saw puzzle at the other end of the living room. She blinked back the tears and continued. "When do I have to decide? How much time do I have? Mary and I have just started talking about options…" Meredith's poise and sophistication had disappeared, erased by panic and pressure. Right now she looked as young and vulnerable as Allison.

"You have as much time as you need," I reached over to pat her clenched hands. "There is no time limit on such an important decision."

"But how do I know what is the right thing?" she cried.

"You'll know what the right thing is when the time comes. God will use your instincts to help you make the right decisions. When you need to decide, you will know what is best for you and your baby."

"You're sure?"

"Confidently confident." Giggling a little, she relaxed and blinked back tears. We sat quietly for a few minutes before her gaze shifted back to me and then dropped to the book in my lap. The color seeped from her face as she stared at the illustration of a tiny human being.

"What's wrong?" I asked. "Are you okay?"

She nodded, gently taking the book from my lap and tracing the picture of a twelve-week fetus with her fingertip. "That's what my other baby looked like when I had the abortion," her voice broke, fresh tears welling up in her eyes. "Can you believe I was dumb enough to believe it was just a clump of cells?"

All other sounds in the room stopped. Everyone stared at Meredith as she smeared tears across her cheek with the back of her hand. Retrieving the book, I said quietly, "Want to go to my room to talk, Meredith?" She seemed to notice the other girls for the first time. "We could talk in private."

"No. It's okay. Maybe they should hear about it." She looked at the girls and said in a choked whisper, "You girls don't know how lucky you are to be here. Getting an abortion was the biggest mistake of my life. But now that it's done, there's absolutely nothing I can do to make it right."

"There's one thing you can do," I interrupted. "You can ask Jesus to forgive you. His forgiveness is big enough for all your mistakes and sins."

Hope and despair played tug-of-war across her face. The guilt has burned its way into her soul. "It's always with me, like a dirty overcoat I can't take off," she said.

"It happened several years ago, didn't it?"

"I was fifteen," she answered. Her eyes stared through me seeing a day five years ago. "Mom told me I was too young to have a baby. I believed her. She said it would kill me and disgrace the family. 'You're lucky we can afford a nice clinic in New York City to take care of things,' she told me."

The words poured out, finding release. She was determined to voice her pain.

Please give me wisdom and grace, Lord. Grace to hear and wisdom to heal.

"I've dreamed about that miserable place a million times," she sobbed. "Mom drove me to the door and dropped me off. I couldn't believe she was leaving me there alone. She gave me the letter from our doctor stating I was pregnant. She said she had some errands to run, that she'd be back for me later."

Lord, how could a mother do that? What incredible pain to carry for five years.

"I didn't think I had a choice. Mom had it all arranged." Her voice shook.

No wonder they are estranged. Meredith is still carrying unforgiveness. What a horrible burden.

"Have any of you ever been inside one of those places?" Meredith asked. Most shook their heads "no." "At first it looks just like any doctor's office. I sat in the waiting room just like I was getting my tonsils checked or something. But then they took me into an examination room—the nurse said it wouldn't take long, that there was 'nothing to it.' The next thing I know I'm in a hospital gown lying on a stretcher, waiting."

Meredith was talking directly to the girls now. I was a spectator watching from the sidelines. All of them quiet, listening intently to Meredith's story.

"I was so scared! I wanted to get dressed and leave. But I was afraid to move. The last thing I remember seeing before they put me to sleep was a big bottle with a hose coming out of it."

Meredith shuddered and swallowed several times before she could continue. The girls leaned forward to hear her next whispered words. "When I woke up, I felt terrible...aching and empty. I threw up. The nurse thought it was the anesthesia, but it was guilt. She made me lay there for awhile before she brought my clothes and an instruction sheet. I felt so sad and all alone."

Everyone was crying with Meredith. Jill, nearly six months pregnant, sobbed, "What happened then?"

Regret and sadness lay deep in Meredith's eyes as she said, "I went outside and sat on a bench. I don't know how long it was until Mom came back. I was numb inside. She wanted to take me shopping. She talked about all the wonderful stores in New York. I guess she was trying to cheer me up. But all I could do was cry. All I wanted to do was go home so I could cry in peace."

Meredith wiped her tears. "All I could do for the next two or three weeks was cry. And then the dreams started. Babies crying. Every night they came until I hated to go to bed. I couldn't forget." She shrugged, resigned to her misery. "I hope none of you ever have to go through something like that."

The silence stretched as we tried to cope with what Meredith had said, "Later," she whispered, "in health class, I found out the truth. It was a baby. No wonder the abortion upset me so!"

Most were quietly sniffling, but Angie was sobbing loudly. And it was she who started to speak, "It's even worse when you're further along. I was six months pregnant when my stepmother figured out why I was gaining so much weight. She took me to a clinic, like the one Meredith went to, only my baby was too big for suction, so they did a saline abortion."

"There were five of us in the room, and I was the last to deliver. I saw all the babies, still and red. I saw mine too—a perfectly formed little boy with blistered skin. As long as I live, I'll never forgive myself for killing my baby. And I'll never forgive that woman for making me do it." Angie's shoulders shook with her sobbing.

Meredith levered herself out of the soft sofa cushions and walked to Angie with her arms outstretched. Angie collapsed in them. Holding each other, the grief swelled and overflowed. The rest wiped eyes, blew noses and stared at the carpet.

I was in shock. The illustrations in my book were not just black and white lines. They were babies, vulnerable and voiceless. God help us! There are people in this nation who make their living destroying the unborn. Suddenly my efforts to help young women safely bring their babies into the world seemed so small beside the destruction.

Anger rose in me like a geyser. Why haven't I realized what is going on? Am I so isolated I can't recognize the inroads evil has made into our country? I'm not doing enough. The House isn't doing enough.

It might have been evening, but I had just gotten my wake-up call. I needed truth—the hard, unpalatable kind—and I knew just who could deliver it.

Judy's Markle's files bulged with information—newspaper articles, court rulings, and reprints from medical journals—all gleaned in two years of research. Determined to understand the abortion issue from both pro and con positions, her own pro-life stand grew out of a rational examination of the facts as well as her religious beliefs.

When I asked for help, she was delighted to share all that she had accumulated. She had tried to educate me before, but I had resisted, thinking abortion was a minor problem and rare occurrence. Now I knew differently. So while I was studying for my final examination in Childbirth Preparation, learning about the safe, live arrival of babies, I was also learning grizzly facts about abortion—how it was performed, who supports it, and how many babies had lost their lives in two short years since the Supreme Court's ruling. I started studying it quietly with only Judy and Jim aware of my interest. It wasn't long until the issue confronted me everywhere I turned. It demanded my attention. And after Mickey, I could no longer ignore it and stay silent...

Melissa and I were in the office discussing a House outing when the phone call came.

"An—ne," a hiccup and a sob split my name into two pieces.

"Yes,"

"This is Mickey." Her voice sounded raw as if she had been crying for hours.

"I'm glad you called. We'll have a bed for you next week."

A low wail was all the response I got.

"Mickey, what's the matter?" Melissa lifted her head from the paper she had been reading and stared at me.

"I...I won't be needing the bed, Anne." Her words were slurred with tears.

"What happened?" I questioned softly. Melissa's lips began to move in silent prayer.

"Bob took me on a date. He didn't tell me where until we got there. It was an abortion clinic…My baby's gone. I killed my baby."

"I'm so sorry, Mickey."

"So am I. Oh, so am I." Lord, she's going to need a lot of love and some good counseling to deal with the guilt I hear in her voice.

"Did Mickey get an abortion?" Melissa asked when I hung up.

"Yes." I shook my head. "I don't understand it. She wanted her baby so much. How could she let Bob talk her into it? Was she that afraid of losing him?"

"That's probably part of it," Melissa said, "but it's not the only reason." Her eyes had a far away look. "I was this close," she measured a short distance between thumb and forefinger, "to getting an abortion. And you know how I feel about it."

"You're kidding!" I cried.

"No, I'm not," she slapped the papers on the desk. "When a girl hears just one side of the story, she forgets about the things she's not being told."

"But how could you even consider such a thing?" I was shocked and my words came out far more judgmental than I intended. That gentle, loving Melissa would even for a minute think of an abortion stunned me.

"It started when I went for a free pregnancy test. Not to a pregnancy center." Melissa shrugged. "One of my roommates gave me the address. I just wanted to be sure I really was pregnant."

"What happened?"

"When the test was positive, they started giving me all these reasons to have an abortion. They made it sound like a simple career decision. Then they made an appointment for me for the next week. They kept calling my baby 'the embryo' or 'the product of conception' like he was just a thing—not a living human being. Pretty soon I found myself thinking maybe I should have an abortion. I mean they'd already made the appointment."

"But you changed your mind. How did that happen?"

Melissa smiled. "It must have been the Lord—something inside me could not accept my decision. I talked to my friends, and they were divided about fifty-fifty, so that didn't really help. In the end, I realized I couldn't go through with it and cancelled my appointment."

"I'm glad."

"Well the lady at the clinic certainly wasn't! You should have heard her. She told me I'd regret not doing it now. That it would only be harder on me if I waited until later. She was so sure she knew the right answer for my problem. You know a lot of people think the counselors are there to direct you to the services you want. Don't believe it! They're there to tell you what they think is right."

"But when you told her that you didn't..."

"Did she back down? No way. I finally hung up on her."

"Have you ever regretted your decision?" I probed.

"Never. Not even for a minute!" She was quick to answer. "My Adam is alive, not tossed in some trash dump. Knowing that is worth the agony of having to part with him." Her face softened, eyes glowing she added, "He'll be three years old in a few months. It doesn't seem that long. No—I have no regrets. Somewhere I have a son named Adam who has a chance to fulfill God's plan for his life."

Now that God had my attention, I began to hear similar stories from other girls who had visited social service agencies. Unless they went to a place like Birthright or a crisis pregnancy center, they were pressured to have an abortion. With each account I learned more about the methods used to convince girls with problem pregnancies to terminate their babies. It filled me with sadness—and anger.

To think about

- A father's love has incredible value and its loss can be crippling. Our whole life is affected by the presence or absence of a father's love.

- Parents severely wound their children when they make choices which are not right in God's eyes. And wounds create thick walls that separate and isolate.

- Truth can be uncomfortable and ugly. We dare not turn from it because it isn't pleasant. But when truth is released into God's hands of forgiveness, He gives great freedom.

- Beware of decisions made to protect an image or a reputation.

"I will say of the Lord,
'He is my refuge and my fortress,
my God, in whom I trust.'"

Psalm 91:2

Chapter 10

Trial by Fire

We had whittled away at the list of requirements the state inspectors left. Mary Copeland and I worked on our record keeping until our files complied with state guidelines. We applied for approval as a maternity home as well as a group home since our population had gradually shifted until three-fourths of our girls were expectant teens. Fire doors were in place on the stairs, and we faithfully practiced our fire drills. God had provided the materials and labor to complete the family room and fill it with a ping-pong table, television, stereo equipment, and a large library of good books that teens would enjoy. The kitchen had also been remodeled with the eating area opening into the new family room.

Only five months and almost all the things on our state "to do" list had been crossed off. So much in so short a time could only have happened because God had intervened.

Good things were happening in Meredith's life as well. After several letters passed between her and her mother, Mrs. Andrews came for a visit. Their relationship was still strained and painful, but they had finally begun the journey toward healing.

Mrs. Andrews brought a gift for Meredith—a beautiful maternity sweater straight from Bonwit Tellers. While it wasn't what Meredith most wanted or needed—like trips to a doctor's office instead of the clinic—it did represent a dramatic change in her mother's attitude. For that, Meredith was very grateful.

Mr. Andrews had been changing as well. He smiled frequently and hugged Meredith every time he visited. Occasionally, he brought casual clothes along so that he and Meredith could take walks, work in the storage shed, or feed the animals. He even began calling Meredith "Morning Glory."

Meredith basked in her father's affection. "He's never been able to have fun with us," she confided. "I think he enjoys leaving his business image behind when he comes to the House. He's even laughing sometimes!"

The only relationship that hadn't improved was the one with Greg. Meredith had asked him to sign the papers relinquishing any claim to their baby—a required step before a child can be placed for adoption. She was sure he would quickly sign the forms and mail them back.

Instead, he informed her that his mother might be interested in taking the baby if it were a girl. "She raised three sons, but she's always wanted a daughter."

"Don't you think that will put quite a bit of strain on our marriage?" Meredith had responded.

"I don't see marriage in our future," was his cool reply.

She was devastated. "Can you believe it, Anne? After all his complaining because I wouldn't get an abortion, now he decides he wants to keep the baby and get rid of me!" The anger in her face changed to fear, "He can't do that can he—give the baby to his mother? I want my baby to have parents who will raise a child with more integrity than Greg has."

"Greg could block your plans to place your baby for adoption," I reluctantly told her.

"Oh no. I don't think I could handle Greg's mother raising the baby."

"Don't worry, Morning Glory," Jim said giving her a big hug. "It'll all work out!"

And so it did. Several weeks later, Greg finally agreed to relinquish his rights to the baby—whether boy or girl. With that settled, Meredith relaxed and focused on her future.

Thanksgiving is truly a time of celebration this year. Your provision has been awesome and abundant. Saturday we still had an abundance of leftovers. Even so, friends in community continued to bring more food to the House probably because they had heard about all our houseguests: girls that had lived with us previously and had nowhere to spend the holiday, current girls who could not go home, family members and friends packed the House.

Shortly after six o'clock we sat down with a boisterous crowd to a feast spread the length of our table. After blessing the food, we reached for fluffy mounds of potatoes, glistening peas and golden turkey, but before we could even take a bite, the upstairs fire alarm sounded. Jim hurried from the room to find the problem and silence the ear-piercing shriek.

In seconds he was back. "Everybody outside," he ordered. "We've got a fire."

It took a few seconds for his words to sink in. Some of the girls giggled, sure it was another of his practical jokes. But I saw the look in his eye. He's serious!

"It's not a drill," Jim barked. "This is the real thing. Now everybody out."

We dashed from the table, each of us knowing exactly what to do because of the state-required fire drills. With the precision that comes with practice, we had everyone—Grandpa, children, guests, girls, dog, and guinea pig—outside and the fire department called in just three minutes. Then we had time to wait and shiver in the cold evening air. Our coats were still in the house—along with most of our shoes. Shelly cradled her guinea pig under her shirt. She had absolutely refused to leave without him.

Thick, gray clouds of smoke swirled around the upstairs windows, and an eerie orange glow spread from room to room as we watched.

I wanted to huddle next to Jim for comfort, but there were frightened girls, a bewildered Grandpa shivering by the heater vent in the front seat of our car, and nervous teens that needed me to be calm and composed. As we moved around hugging and comforting members of the group, our eyes would meet. I saw in Jim's eyes the same helplessness I felt.

The volunteer fire department arrived trailing a long line of cars filled with neighbors and friends who had heard about the blaze on the police scanner. The next few hours were a blur of activity—wrapping a shivering form in a blanket...this can't be happening...giving my shoes to Lara...it has to be a bad dream... organizing the girls into caravans of cars which carried them to a local Baptist church...Lord, how can You allow such a disaster?... and standing with Jim in our soggy front yard as the firemen worked feverishly...it's Thanksgiving weekend!

Jim and I followed the last of the girls to the church. So many needs—temporary housing, emotional support, and fresh clothing—kept us from dwelling on the disaster. Crawling wearily from our van, we braced ourselves for the barrage of questions we knew was waiting for us in the fellowship hall. The questions started as soon as they spotted us.

"How bad is it?"

"Can we go home?"

Before we could do much more than reassure them that it would work out, several of the volunteer firemen arrived with our meal. They had found it untouched on our table, packed it up, and transported it to us. The delicious smells, delivered by soot-covered Good Samaritans, wrapped us in comfort and encouragement. Even in the middle of trouble, You send reminders of Your care and love!

They had even brought along the card box, which sat on our table. We pulled a card from that box every evening before eating. When we had all gathered around the table and prayed over our meal a second time, Melissa drew a card and read, "Do mountains move your faith or does your faith move mountains?" Tears and laughter flowed together as we realized God had hand-delivered, via the fireman, a challenge to stand strong.

Still, part of me was crying inside and worrying about our future. But another part of me watched in awe as our girls worked as a team, helping with the meal, caring for each other and sharing hope. Meredith was especially busy—pouring beverages, getting desserts from the kitchen, and clearing dishes. Sometimes it takes a crisis to reveal a person's potential. And this is the young woman who considered her roommates slobs.

The Red Cross volunteers arrived just as we finished dinner bringing news of another blessing: the local J.C. Penney store was providing each girl with a nightgown and a set of underwear. And the Red Cross was giving each girl a change of clothing as well. Thank You, Lord, for demonstrating Your loving care to the girls.

While the girls were excitedly chattering about their new clothes, the fire chief pulled Jim and me aside to say, "I've got bad news. There is little doubt that the fire was deliberately set."

We were stunned. Jim was quick to deny the possibility, "There is not a girl in the House who would do something like that. You must have made a mistake."

The chief shook his head, "Sorry, Mr. Pierson. But all the evidence points to arson. You'd better talk to the girls who have the bedroom in the back corner. That's where it started."

"What do we do, Jim?" Fresh tears clogged my throat. "How will we ever tell the girls it was arson?"

Shaking his head he replied, "No idea. God will show us what to say when the time comes. As to who did it, He'll reveal that when it's time as well."

The next wave of blessings came while we were still trying to recover from the chief's devastating news: friends invited us into their homes and spare bedrooms. Soon Grandpa, Aunt May, the girls and our children all had places to stay. Jim, Melissa, Cindy and I would camp out in our new family room to prevent vandals from destroying what the fire hadn't.

We had just about matched everyone with temporary housing when the minister of our host church pulled us aside and said, "One of your girls is in the sanctuary crying. She really needs someone."

It was Lara, temporarily housed with us over the long holiday weekend before being placed in a foster home. Jim went back to the others saying, "I'll make sure she has a nice quiet place to stay tonight. You talk to her. She's probably scared to death. Too many adjustments to make too fast."

Ten minutes later, Lara and I slipped into the far end of the fellowship hall away from the girls. Both of us had red-rimmed eyes—one set staring at the floor and the other beckoning Jim to come. He hurried toward us.

"Lara won't be needing that bed, Jim."

Briefly the second set of eyes lifted and looked at him. "I set the fire," Lara confessed in a hoarse whisper. I recognized the look on Jim's face. The same pain and bewilderment that had washed through me.

"Why, Lara?" Jim asked just as I had.

Tears dripped from her chin and distorted her words as she explained, "I thought if you got mad at me, they would make my daddy come."

Jim and I wrapped her in a three-way hug. Stepping into the role of substitute father, Jim reassured and comforted her. "We love you, honey. And we forgive you," he whispered in her ear. And he meant every word. Despite the financial pressure that had just increased because of fire damage, even though emotional pain was carving lines in his face, Jim chose to forgive Lara, not holding onto bitterness or blame. The acrid smell of smoke clung to Jim's shirt reminding us of the fire's devastation. Yet Jim's attention was on Lara and her pain. Jesus, You bore the consequences of our actions for us. How awesome! The impact of that moment has remained vivid in my mind. It changed me forever.

"Really?" Her eyes searched Jim's and then mine. I could feel the tension leave her muscles when she saw nothing but love in our faces. My heart hurts for her, Father. So desperate for a father's love that she does desperate things.

It was hard sending Lara off with a policewoman to a juvenile holding facility.

"It was supposed to be a little fire that we would discover quickly," I murmured sadly. "But she timed it wrong—everyone was downstairs for dinner. And she made the mistake of starting it in the room where the nail polish remover was spilled last week. Once it hit that spot it really took off."

"Poor little girl. Let's wait to tell the others until they've moved back to the House."

I nodded. "Most are leaving now for their temporary quarters. They won't notice." But Meredith did…

"Where did Lara go?" she asked. "I didn't see her after dinner."

Deciding she could be trusted to keep the news to herself, I told her what had happened. "Please don't tell anyone yet." I concluded, "We'll talk about it when we're all back together. Pray for her though. She has lots of problems before and now they're even bigger."

Meredith scowled angrily, but reluctantly nodded her head in agreement before turning back to what remained of our group. Within minutes her hostess arrived to take her home. Clutching her Red Cross kit and J.C. Penney bag, she waddled to the waiting car. I realized Meredith's time with us was almost up. Even her long baggy coat couldn't camouflage the bulge at her middle. I hope she doesn't choose tonight to go into labor. I've had more than enough excitement for one day.

Finally, the firemen said it was safe to enter the House. The smell of burned wood irritated my eyes and nose. Ceilings sagged with water damage and walls reeked with smoke. Upstairs, several bedrooms had charred doors and skeletal remains of furniture.

To our delight, we found the new wing undamaged with no signs of flames, smoke or water.

Postscript

Holidays demanded a lot of grace. Only the girls who had no home or who had an unsafe home remained behind. Jim, our daughters and I longed to be with our families during these special times, but there were always girls who needed us because there was no place else for them to go. Instead of festivity, the atmosphere was heavy with pain and loneliness. And no one experienced that more than Angie...

"Dad called. He's coming to pick me up and take me to Gram's for Thanksgiving!" Angie's eyes sparkled with anticipation and joy. "She always gives me a great big hug and a kiss before she even shuts the door." I could hear her in the family room telling everyone about the day to come. "Dad and I will play games and watch TV. It'll be great."

My eyes only partially opened, I slipped down the stairs at seven Thanksgiving morning. Mentally reviewing all that needed to be done in the kitchen, I almost missed Angie seated quietly on the chair facing the front drive. Dressed in her best red and white outfit with matching bow in her hair, she was ready and waiting for her dad to arrive.

At 7:30, when the bacon was crisp and the eggs scrambled, I invited her to join us for breakfast. "No, Dad will be here any time now. Gram will want to stuff me with food all day. I'll just wait here."

At 11:00, with the turkey turning brown in the oven, I urged her to at least nibble on some toast. She shook her head, "I don't want to get messy. Dad won't want to wait. I'm fine."

At 4:00, with our meal sitting hot and tempting on the table, I invited her to join us. "No thanks. Dad promised. He'll be here soon."

At 9:00, Angie sat sobbing on the couch. Finally, I convinced her to come to the kitchen and eat some leftovers. The night was no darker than my thoughts about irresponsible parents and the damage they do. An entire day Angie had waited, trusting in her father's promise and hoping for a special family holiday. Disillusioned and depressed, this disaster would only make it more difficult for her to believe in a Heavenly Father Who loves her and keeps His promises.

To think about

- Satan uses deception to confuse us into thinking his way is the only way to solve a problem even when someone will get hurt. God always provides a way out that is good for us, as well as anyone else involved. That's God's way.

- Sex before marriage puts lust ahead of commitment. Rarely does the commitment work out, and the individuals are left with the results of broken relationship.

- Forgiveness and love are key elements when we have been hurt by another. We need to forgive for our well-being, as well as our enemies.

- Fathers are vital. Their love and care shape a child's sense of worth and increase their capacity to trust. Children will do desperate things to get and keep a father's attention.

"God works all things together for good
for those who love Him and are called
according to His purpose."

Romans 8:28

Chapter 11

All Things for Good

Jim and I surveyed the losses from the fire the next morning. They towered over us like the sheer, unscalable wall of a cliff. Two bedrooms were totaled. A third had a small portion that might be salvageable. Our family was disrupted as the girls scattered throughout the community and lost contact with each other.

Romans 8:28 says, "God works all things together for good for those who love Him and are called according to His purpose." It's hard to see how burning our house can be turned to our good. We've lost so much…

God answered within a few days. In fact, He started before I even asked—with the people in the community who responded to news of the fire. We became aware, as never before, of the community's love and support for us. Food, clothing, places to stay, transportation, money, paint and building supplies, not to mention the priceless gifts of time and labor—the outpouring was overwhelming. Jim organized an all-volunteer crew so well that within a week we were able to bring every girl home and return to our daily routine.

Not only were the rooms fixed, they were far better than they had been originally: new carpets, complete sets of matching furniture and color coordinated accessories. They barely resembled the mismatched rooms the girls abandoned a week ago.

And for those special personal items that couldn't be replaced—things like photographs and books—a wonderful couple stepped in to salvage all they could. Bob and Joyce worked one-on-one with each girl to lovingly restore all they could and to gently help each girl work through the loss of what couldn't be saved. Evening after evening, they arrived at the House to mend possessions and hearts until every girl had received their loving attention.

Another young couple was Tom and Betsy. While this couple had neither money to give nor skills to help with repairs, they provided something equally valuable—empathy. Because a fire had completely destroyed their home several years earlier, they understood the questions Jim and I struggled with. Why had God permitted the fire? How would the fire affect our ministry? Tom and Betsy had faced similar questions and could now pray for us in ways that no one else could. They reassured us of God's perfect plan, His grace, and His provision. It was wonderful to have new friends who understood and who would walk with us through the bewildering weeks following the fire.

Another answer to my "what good can come" question was actually proof from an earlier disaster. The state inspections we had so resented had worked for our greater good. It was because of their insistence that ugly, steel fire doors be installed on the stairs that the fire had not spread to other parts of the house. Without them we could easily have lost everything. The empty attic also minimized the damage; if that third floor had been stuffed with boutique and storage items, the fire would have found fresh fuel to keep burning. The smoke alarms we had grudgingly installed alerted us to the danger far more quickly than if we had waited to smell the smoke. And of course, there were the state mandated fire drills as well—what kind of chaos and precious time had they saved us in those minutes after we discovered the fire?

God had obviously used the state's intervention for our ultimate good and well-being. While we had fussed about wasted time and money, He was ensuring our future safety. Once the realization of His care had seeped into my mind, I meekly acknowledged His was a better plan and repented of my attitude toward the state regulations. How humbling to look back and see that I had bitterly resented the very thing God would use to save the ministry.

Meredith, Kate, and Robin returned home just a few days after the fire since theirs had been the least damaged bedroom. Meredith was barely in the door before she asked about Lara. "I can't get her out of my mind. I was really upset that you would ask me to pray for her – pray for someone who'd do a thing like that. But I did. And you know what? Now I just feel sorry for her. Is she going to jail?"

"Lara's been placed in an adolescent psychiatric facility."

Relieved that Lara was being helped, Meredith poured her energy into getting the House back in order—at least for the next several days until she started a different kind of labor. And, of course, she started that labor in the middle of the night.

This delivery was a first of its kind. Meredith was the first girl who had completed childbirth classes with me, and her baby was the first birth I attended since receiving my certification. It was a wonderful first for all three of us. The delivery went smoothly— just six hours from beginning to end. Meredith never lost control, breathing the way we'd practiced and working with each contraction. Her baby girl was pink and healthy—as alert as any newborn I'd ever seen.

Both nurses and doctor commended Meredith's preparation and cooperative attitude. Our childbirth classes had definitely paid off.

Meredith reached out with eager arms to hold her daughter for the first time. "She's perfect...so perfect," she murmured over and over as tears trickled down her cheeks. "I'm just so glad she's okay," Meredith confessed with a wobbly smile.

She's been afraid. Afraid that the earlier abortion would hurt this baby. She's never talked about it, but she must have thought about it a lot.

It was quite awhile before Meredith allowed the nurse to take her daughter to the nursery. Meredith was still being wheeled from the delivery room when she said, "I want to call Mom and Dad and tell them about my daughter." Since she had not had anesthesia she called as soon as she reached her room. She was smiling when she hung up. Apparently both parents were as pleased as Meredith that the baby had arrived safely.

No one mentioned Greg. Since he had finally agreed to sign the adoption papers, he had dropped out of the picture, no longer figuring in any of Meredith's plans for the future.

With that, Meredith had relaxed and briefly considered raising the baby herself. Her parents' attitude had changed enough she was fairly certain she could count on their support, but she soon decided not to. "Adoption is best for my baby," she told me confidently. "And I need to finish my education, figure out what's in the future for me before I try to handle the responsibilities of motherhood."

She wrote a beautiful letter to her daughter telling her how much she was loved and explaining that she wanted a loving home with two parents for her. We encouraged all of our girls who chose adoption to write a letter to their babies. The girls were going to grieve for their babies and the letters helped with closure—something very necessary in grief situations. It also helped them clarify and explain why adoption is best for them and for their children. Writing it down helped them on the special days—like birthdays—when the pain is worst. Those are the days when they need to remember why they made the choice they did.

The letter is also valuable for the children. One day they will wonder why their birthmothers didn't parent them, questioning whether they were loved and wanted. The letter can reassure them that the decision to place them with an adoptive couple was made out of a genuine and sacrificial love. It lets them know that their mothers parted with them reluctantly and only after a lot of prayer and planning.

Meredith's letter told of the love and pain and hope for the future as beautifully as any I've seen. Splotched with tears and tucked into the envelope with a lingering caress, Meredith gave her daughter the gift of a family.

A short nap and a shower were all I had time for between leaving Meredith in the hospital and my afternoon appointments. My groggy, sleep-deprived body wanted to turn that nap into a Rip van Winkle sleep, but the people coming for my first appointment were driving all the way from Washington, D.C. To ask them to reschedule would cause major inconvenience. Besides which, it was my father who had set it up.

Dave Anton, a friend and fellow pastor, was encountering quite a few difficulties as he counseled a family in his church. The parents and their pregnant sixteen-year-old daughter could not come to any kind of agreement, and Dave was just about out of options. So Poppy called to see if I would talk to the family and Dave.

Poppy warned me that Christina, the daughter, might refuse to come. I cautiously set aside several hours to spend with the Calders, thinking this would not be a short or easy counseling session.

Jim ushered all four into the office promptly at 1 pm. Christina, body rigid, mouth set in a grim line, acted as if she had been forced to come at gun point. Physically present, she was emotionally absent.

I tried talking to Christina, but she proved even more difficult than Allison. As far as Christina was concerned, none of us were worth talking to. I needed to discover why her parents had come to me for help, and I wasn't going to get the answers from her.

After giving Christina the pre-admission forms to fill out at my desk, I began questioning her parents. Their family life had been close and harmonious—near storybook perfection—until Christina was fifteen. That's when she met and became infatuated with Michael, a young man who lived a kind of wild bachelor existence with his divorced father.

"Michael's just not the kind of boy we wanted her to date," Mrs. Calder said.

"We don't have anything against him," said her husband and then proceeded to list all the things they did have against him. "He doesn't go to church. He's not a good student. Has no future except pumping gas, which he does now part-time."

"He runs wild. Doesn't keep decent hours," added Mrs. Calder.

"And he drinks even though he's only sixteen," concluded Mr. Calder. "He's not good for Christina. But now she's gotten herself pregnant and wants us to let her get married." Tears glistened in his eyes as he added, "She's just a little girl herself. How can she expect us to approve?"

As they continued to share, I began to get a picture of what was happening in their home. Mr. Calder, frustrated and frightened for his daughter's future, lost his temper frequently and said things he regretted when he later cooled down. Mrs. Calder's reaction to the tension was very different. She had become cold and distant, pulling away from painful reality and into herself. Wrapped in their hurt, they could not reach out to Christina to give her the love and acceptance she needed.

If not for their religious and moral convictions, the Calders, like the Andrews, would have pushed for an abortion. Fortunately, they realized that was not a viable option, that it would only add more guilt and pain. Not one of them wanted that—not the parents, not their pastor, and certainly not Christina.

I'm not going to make any progress with Christina while her parents are in the room. Perhaps refreshments with Aunt May…

Closing the door behind them, I turned to Christina. "Tell me about Michael."

"Nobody calls him Michael except my parents." Ice cycles hung from her words. "Everyone calls him Mick. He's a lot nicer than they make him sound. I love him and I'm going to marry him!" Mixed with the glaring spite in her eyes was a gleam of anticipation.

She wants me to challenge her. To go on the defensive. I'll try the offensive instead.

"You don't want to be here, do you?"

"No, I don't!" she shot back. "I only came because Pastor Anton asked me to. I don't want to live here. I want to live with Mick."

"We won't take you if you don't want to be here," I smiled sympathetically. "Don't worry. Nobody can force you to come."

She relented slightly at this news and smiled stiffly before glancing around the room.

"Can we at least talk until it's time to leave?" I asked as her gaze swung back in my direction. "Tell me about your parents. You're pretty angry with them, aren't you?"

"My parents are hypocrites!" she shouted. Her face flushed and fists clenched. "'Love everyone'—everyone but Mick, that is. They hate him, because his mother is black. Liars. Hypocrites. They only love the ones just like them."

Uh-oh. Some facts the Calders left out.

"Are you allowed to see him at all?" I asked.

"No," she relaxed a little. "But you heard them. I sneak out."

"Did you know Mick would be welcome to come to see you here? Boyfriends have visiting privileges."

I'm almost sure I saw a flicker of interest. "It'd probably help to be away from your parents—have a little breathing space."

I could see she was thinking about it, but her only outward response was a grunt.

"One question I always ask girls in your situation is 'What are your options?'" I listed them starting with the ones she didn't want to consider. "You can stay at home."

"No, I don't want to live with them."

"You want to live with Mick?"

She nodded enthusiastically.

"Do he and his father have room for you? Or can you and Mick afford an apartment of your own?"

Her head swung slowly from side to side as tears rolled. She really has no options and she knows it. Her defiance is senseless.

"Here's what I can do," I said softly as we heard Jim leading the group toward the office. "I'll hold a place for you as long as I can. You think about it. Call me by next Tuesday and tell me what you want to do. Remember, this is your decision—no one else's."

The Calders' looks of anticipation evaporated when I said, "Christina is going to think about what she wants and let me know if she wants to come to the House." They were hoping for a quick solution—one that would get rid of the anxiety and tension.

"Thanks for fitting us in to your schedule, Anne," Pastor Anton said. "I'll be in touch in a few days."

He at least accepts the fact that Christina needs to have some control in the situation. I doubt he expects her to come any more than I do.

Christina proved us wrong. Just two days later, she called me, "I've decided to come. You did promise Mick could visit."

"Yes, I did and he can."

"I'll come after Christmas."

Christmas brought a mixture of joy and sorrow. Almost all signs of the fire had been removed. The new family room was filled with fragrant greens and homemade decorations. In one corner a giant, donated evergreen stood guard over a growing pile of gifts. While we often struggled to make ends meet during the rest of the year, Christmas released a generous outpouring. Wouldn't it be wonderful if it was Christmas in our hearts all year—no more lack, no more going without paychecks!

We were looking forward to Allison and Candy's arrival for a holiday visit—a long weekend to rejoice in Allison's progress and fuss over Candy.

But we faced good-byes as well. Meredith had stayed with us for several weeks after her daughter's adoption. We had walked with her through the first stages of her grief and now she felt ready to move ahead. For her that meant returning home and enrolling for her final two semesters of college at the University of Pennsylvania. What a radical change in her relationship with her family had come because she refused to compromise what she knew to be right! Her parents were treating her like the adult she was—and giving her the warmth and affection she'd missed in childhood. Even her "perfect" older sister, Candice, relented enough to make the trip with Mrs. Andrews to the hospital to say goodbye to the baby.

The Andrews made moving Meredith home a family occasion. Mr. Andrews arrived with her brother, Tim, to welcome her home. They brought gifts for Jim and me, Grandpa, Holly, Shelly and Aunt May. When we weren't looking they slipped an envelope onto my desk which we found after they left. In it was a large check for the House. Mrs. Andrews pulled me aside to apologize, "Please forgive me for trying to force Meredith to have an abortion. You just don't know how it breaks a mother's heart to see her daughter make such a terrible mistake," she explained. "I felt so helpless and alone. And all that terrible guilt and blame pressing down on me."

After watching so many mothers' anger and tears at the news of a teen daughter's pregnancy, I thought I did understand what Mrs. Andrews had gone through. Still, she had a point—I hadn't experienced it myself.

Jim, of course, managed to slip away after meeting Tim but before they had all the suitcases in the car. My throat tightened and tears hung on my lashes as I hugged Meredith one last time. Giving me a kiss, she said, "You folks are the ultimate guardian angels. Thank you for being here for me—and for putting up with my moods. I love you!" A last wave from the back seat of the Mercedes and she was gone.

Before any tears could spill over, Jim reappeared, grinning like Santa himself saying, "Tom and Betsy have something to tell you." I looked at the beloved couple standing in front of me, hoping I had already guessed what their news was. For several months, we had been praying about and discussing the possibility of opening another home. None of us liked the idea of turning girls away who needed help, but with a firm limit of twelve at the House, it was a real necessity. We even had a second house lined up in Lititz—a town just thirty minutes away. All we lacked was the right houseparents.

Tom grinned at me, "We've decided to take the job."

"Wonderful!" I gathered Becky into a hug. "You fit the role perfectly. Plenty of love, great instincts for dealing with teens.

And you know what you're taking on—the time spent with us has prepared you well!

Although this gift didn't come wrapped in festive paper and a red bow, it was my favorite one that year.

Postscript

Meredith went on to graduate school and received a degree in special education. She taught for several years in a Christian school. For years, it looked as if she would not marry. Then, in her late thirties, she surprised everyone by marrying a wonderful Christian man. They have five children—three boys and two girls—who are thriving in their secure, loving environment.

Meredith continues to grow in the Lord, her radiance evidence of the joy and peace she has found in Him. She often meets with young women facing the same difficult decision she did, sharing her own adoption experience with them and telling them of Jesus' love.

Mr. and Mrs. Andrews have the joy of knowing that, because of Meredith's unselfish decision, a young woman somewhere in this world is enjoying the gift of life. Mrs. Andrews also has the joy that comes with making a commitment to Christ. Meredith's time at the House has borne much fruit.

To think about

- Often a disaster will pull people together in ways nothing else would.

- When God brings restoration, it is always better than it was before.

- God's provision often comes in ways that surprise us.

- In all our years of ministry, we have never had a young woman place a child in adoption who didn't truly love the child.

- Praying for our enemies does amazing things for our own hearts.

"The purposes of a person's heart are deep waters,
but one who has insight draws them out."

Proverbs 20:5

Chapter 12

Christina

Christina moved in with us in early January, just days before Melissa and I drove to Washington, D.C. to be part of the March for Life. Joining fifty thousand people who came to protest the Supreme Court's decision that opened the door for legalized abortion, I was injected with fresh determination to fight with every weapon I could muster.

Every new fact I discovered increased my fire. Each new story of a girl pressured into abortion fueled the flames until the abortion issue consumed much of my time and energy. I heard...

"They said it was a glob of cells."

"I didn't really want to have the abortion, but there were no other options."

"My boyfriend said he would break up with me..."

"My parents/friends said it was the only way out of a bad situation."

"I didn't know it was a baby."

I grew angrier with each new incident. Our society isn't offering pregnant girls much of a choice. They convince young women that the best thing to do is take the life of their child and then abandon them to suffer the aftermath alone. No help for the pain and guilt. I want to tell the abortion advocates about the Merediths and Angies who carry anger and regrets for years. I want to be involved, to make a difference!

I went to Right to Life meetings to learn how others combated this one-sided pro-abortion counseling. Eventually my passion for these bewildered, pressured young women boiled up and over into every speech I gave—every invitation to talk about the House of His Creation, I used to share about the tragedy of abortion. Much more of my time was spent away from the House and much of that time was dedicated to the pro-life movement.

I became too involved with the issue—and because of it I did not see Christina's inability to adjust to life at the House. I knew she was fighting me over the Bible Studies. Every Wednesday I confronted her, "Christina, all the questions must be answered and answered completely. Until this assignment is done satisfactorily, there will be no TV." The discipline varied as I tried to find appropriate consequences—missing a shopping trip or adding extra chores. But the extra chores were done no better than the Bible Studies. Was this how all her work was being done? I checked with Melissa.

"She's been goofing off since she arrived," Melissa summarized. "She has a massive chip on her shoulder and reacts negatively whenever she is told to do something. All she wants to do is talk with Mick on the phone or have him come visit."

"So her attitude's been all around bad?" I questioned.

Melissa spread her hands and shrugged, "About the same as at the table."

Uh, oh, there's obviously been a problem at meal times you haven't picked up on, Anne! You'd better give more time and attention to your girls.

It wasn't hard to see once I choose to look. In an attempt to be "cool," Christina acted bored and contemptuous. When little Carrie enthusiastically described a school project, Christina cut her off with "What a stupid idea!" When Melissa requested the salt, she shoved it in her general direction. When she poked fun at Jesse's layette as "second-hand junk," Jim scowled, and I knew I had to do something immediately.

I was almost positive that Christina was testing us—watching for signs of the same heavy-handed methods her parents had used. Heavy-handed was definitely not our style, but setting firm boundaries was. Christina was past due to find that out. After dinner, I called her into my office.

"I don't know why I have to do all the work," she huffed. "I'm pregnant. Even my mother didn't make me scrub bathtubs."

"Christina, most of the girls here are pregnant," I reminded gently. "They all do their share of the chores. Not only do we expect you to do yours, but to do them with reasonably good humor. You cannot take your moods out on the others—in such a large family we must be especially considerate of each other."

Her only response was a blank stare.

"We think you're a special person with wonderful potential. There is a life available to you that is filled with all kinds of possibilities. We'd like to help you discover that life, if we can—in the meantime, you have to abide by the rules of the House. By coming here you made that choice."

She jerked her hand out of mine and sat rigidly staring straight ahead. "I've been told that today's chores are not done, and you have been on discipline every week about your Bible studies. Until you are caught up—chores completed satisfactorily and Bible studies finished on time—your phone privileges are suspended, and the only visitors you may have will be your family. You should be caught up in…"

Leaping up she wailed, "You can't do that! I won't stay here. You can't make me." Fists clenched and red-faced she shouted, "I'll go home before I'll let you do that." She moved too quickly for me to stop her. Her wild sobs echoed in the hallway.

"Let her go, Anne," Jim's calm voice stopped my mad dash after her. "She's not going anywhere. She's got no place to go." He rubbed my shoulder consolingly. "Give her time and space to vent her frustrations; then reassure her. She'll settle down and listen."

I stood, hand on the banister, listening to the receding sobs. It was hard, but Jim was right. I retreated to the office to pray.

Christina made good on her threat, calling her parents and asking to move home. They wisely refused—she had chosen to stay at the House until the baby's birth and here she would have to stay. She would live with the choice she had made.

With all other options cut off, she got to work. It took just three days to complete all the neglected chores, and that Wednesday her Bible study was turned in and done well. The privilege of talking to Mick was a powerful motivator. Although it didn't make her any less rude to me, in general, her behavior did improve.

Reality told her to tolerate us, so she did. That did not mean she wanted anything to do with the love and acceptance we offered. Only when the Lord provided a breakthrough would that change. So that's how I began to pray for her.

His answer came from an unexpected source—as it so often did. And while the Lord was reaching through Christina's hard shell, He threw in a lesson for me as well.

To think about

- Anger can cause us to do things that are out of God's will for our lives.

- Do you love someone enough to hold up a standard for them, even if they get mad at you?

- Is a cause, even a righteous one, consuming you to the point where you lose your focus?

"How priceless is your unfailing love,
O God! People take refuge in the
shadow of your wings."

Psalm 36:7

Chapter 13

Getting Back on Course

"You're kidding!" I laughed.

"No, I'm not," Jim's smile had a decided smirk to it.

"What made you think of cows? She hates cleaning up her own messes, and you have her mucking out stalls?"

"For your information, she loves it." Jim grinned with pleasure. "I noticed the only time she softens is when she's stroking Jennifer or playing with one of the cats." Jim's shrug was overly nonchalant—if he had been wearing suspenders, his thumbs would have been tucked in them with his elbows cocked. "So I said to myself, 'Why not try her with the cows?' I need the help, and she needs a job that makes her feel good."

"But has she scooped out the manure?" I questioned skeptically.

"You watch. She's out there now making like Old McDonald and loving every minute of it."

We'll see. Christina and the cows—it doesn't seem possible…

Christina slid into the last open chair at the supper table and breathlessly announced, "I cleaned the cows' stalls and fed them. I think they already know me." Pride and pleasure oozed from her voice. She said something positive! It's the first time since she arrived. How like Jim to find the key no one else would think of!

We knock ourselves out trying to reach her heart, and he matches her with the cows.

But cows couldn't do it all. Even velvet-eyed bovines couldn't break down all her thick heart-barriers. Abscessed pockets of hostility still needed to be lanced and cleaned. Then there was her obsession with a most unsuitable young man. Mick's just not a good candidate for husband or father right now. If only Christina would find other interests—something to displace Mick. Then perhaps she would accept the love we are offering.

Proof that her walls were developing cracks appeared several weeks later during quiet time. Classical music flowed from the family room. Peeking in, I saw Christina seated at our scarred, hand-me-down piano. What beautiful sounds from a girl who insisted she had no musical interest or talent.

I decided to tip-toe away before she noticed me—attention could make her withdraw again. Soon, though, she was playing every day, and we would gather around to watch and listen. When her concerts began to include requests from the audience, I knew the cracks had become major fissures. The day a smile broke through these widening holes when I complimented her, I felt certain the walls were doomed.

Not that they would topple just yet. The House rules still made her bristle. Any and all use of authority or discipline infuriated her, but her chores were reasonably thorough and done on time.

Gradually, other improvements appeared. Instead of rote answers, her Bible studies contained insights and honesty even, at times, doubts and fears. We were indeed making progress when Christina allowed herself to be vulnerable, admitting she had questions about God and her relationship with Him. Then one evening, she shyly asked to join me in a game of Monopoly™. We played this mutual favorite many times in the next weeks. While we hopped over St. Charles Place, skittered past Go To Jail, and landed on the Reading Railroad, Christina talked about her hopes and dreams.

"Anne, a baby's a big responsibility and a lot work. Do you think Mick and I are ready to be parents?"

Hallelujah! Oh, Lord, I want to dance and shout. Help me to stay calm. And not to say too much! "I think God will show you if now is the right time for you to parent."

Christina fiddled with the tiny silver top hat, which was always her game piece of choice. "I've been wondering about adoption. Maybe that would be better. Mick isn't … I mean he doesn't…" She frowned and shook her head. "I can't put it into words. I'm just not sure…"

"Well, you know him better than we do."

She nodded, "That's why I've been wondering…um, do you think adoption might be a good idea?"

Oh, how I want to tell her that her parents are right about Mick. He's not coming to the House much any more. Even his phone calls have dropped off. "I think if you have doubts, it would be wise to explore all your options—including adoption."

"Yeah, I guess I will. Thanks, Anne."

"You're welcome." Guide her, Lord. Help her find the answers she's seeking. And help me not to give quick and easy advice!

A week or so later, over another game of Monopoly, Christina shared how her search was going. "Mick really blew up when I suggested adoption. He was really angry. He scared me."

As her relationship with Mick deteriorated, her attitude toward her parents blossomed. At first, she had sulked and balked at the thought of her parents coming for a visit. Now, she practically wriggled with pleasure. They were thoroughly delighted to have the "old" Christina back.

"Before Michael, she was so pleasant and loving," Mrs. Calder smiled and blinked back joyous tears. "You don't know how wonderful it is to see her smile at me again."

God's love was truly working a miraculous transformation. Christina started looking for ways to help: cooking with Aunt May in the kitchen, doing chores that weren't on her assigned list, and tending her cows with loving care. What a joy it was to watch!

God was working miracles throughout the ministry. The Lititz house opened its doors and almost immediately filled with six pregnant girls. Tom and Betsy were doing every bit as good a job as we had expected. On paper, the additional expenses of this new house should have created an undertow strong enough to drown us all in red ink, but each new expense was matched by a miraculous provision. We never had extra, but for genuine needs, God always had an answer.

Each time He answered our need, our faith grew. Instead of just reading about miracles that occurred centuries before, the girls saw them happening. Aunt May, Melissa, Jim and I became God's Technicolor™, three-dimensional demonstrations of His love, patience, and willingness to use less-than-perfect people. Our obedience, even if the attempts were often fumbling, led to dramatically changed lives.

And, like the cherry perched on top of a sundae, we would soon have government approval as well.

Not that life was one thrilling miracle after another nor did the House always hum with healthy, loving relationships. There were girls who just wouldn't abide by the rules—the discipline and structure grated and rubbed too harshly against rebellious natures and embittered spirits. Not even Jim could find a key to every girl's heart. Many times we shared God's love and faithfulness, and the only response was glazed eyes and huge yawns.

Sadness smothered the House at times as well. One of our girls delivered a stillborn infant. Another precious baby, born prematurely, died several days after birth. The pain and grief that come with death are very hard to handle, especially for the young. Without God's grace, these times of grief would have been overwhelming.

I was still spending time away from the House involved in Right to Life activities. Time after time, I was away when a crisis arose. My conscience nagged me about this until I became uneasy and defensive. So my reaction was predictable the night Randy, our new pastor, took me aside after a board meeting.

"Something has been bothering me, Anne," he began gently. "God called you to help adolescent girls—to love and nurture them through painful decisions and frightening times. I know you feel deeply about the abortion issue. I admire your passion and sense of urgency, but is this what God has called you to do?"

How dare he question how I use my time! What's wrong with acting on my convictions? Would he rather I sat on the sidelines and shrugged my shoulders? Why shouldn't I help wherever I can? Abortion isn't going to go away if Christians ignore it. "What I do is important," I replied hotly. "Somebody's got to fight for those girls and their babies."

"I agree. But is that someone you?" was his soft response.

When I had cooled off—a few days later—I replayed Randy's words in my mind. He didn't say it was wrong for me to be involved, only questioned if it was the best use of my time. Lord, where do you want my energies invested?

It didn't take long for God to answer: Randy was right. I had moved beyond what God had called me to do. I was outside of His plans and desires. The girls came first. The abortion issue was secondary.

But how do I back off? It troubles me so deeply. I hate what it does to the girls as well as to the innocent babies. I can't just turn my back on this issue.

Gradually, I withdrew from many of my public roles in the movement and concentrated my efforts behind the scenes. The speaking I did was once again to support the home and the young women we served. A sense of peace returned—I had discovered the right balance, I was back in line with God's plan.

Since I am prone to ignore my own limitations, I placed my activities under the loving supervision of a wonderful husband and others who knew me and who knew God's plans for the House of His Creation. What a sense of security and freedom there is in having godly friends and committed board members watching over me!

To think about

- Most people need a listening ear, not advice.

- Coming under someone's authority is an important part of all our lives. There are times when we are in authority and times when we are under authority. We must learn to be under authority before we will use authority wisely.

- God's transformations are rarely sudden and usually occur in the secret places of our heart.

"But seek first his kingdom and his righteousness,
and all these things will be given to you as well."

Matthew 6:33

Chapter14

Miracles

I was elbow deep in Bible Studies when Christina appeared at the door, red-rimmed eyes and lines of deep pain etched on her face.

"Christina, what's happened?" I slipped my arm around her and drew her to the couch. She collapsed against the cushions sobbing noisily for several minutes. All I could do was supply a steady stream of tissues to mop up the overflow.

Finally, she emerged from her tissues and announced bitterly, "It's all over with Mick! I'm never going to see him again. I can't believe I ever thought he loved me. What a fool I've been. What a jerk he is!"

"Want to tell me about it?" Adolescent girls—they renounce boyfriends "forever," but the banished usually return within the week, or day, sometimes the hour. If I had a nickel for every spat with a boyfriend, we could pay off the mortgage.

"He just informed me he doesn't want to get married," Christina mumbled through a fresh layer of tissues. "He wants me to live with him and take care of him and his 'son.'" Her chin lifted pugnaciously, "Of course, he's sure it's a boy! And if I don't like that arrangement—why he'll keep the baby himself. He wants his son more than he wants me!"

Christina's tear-streaked face crumpled. She sobbed uncontrol-
lably against my shoulder. All I could do was stroke her hair while
holding her in a protective hug. Conversation was impossible until
she released some of the heart-breaking pain. Finally, she raised
her head and swiped at her cheeks. Tears trembled on her chin.

"What am I going to do?" bewilderment and disillusion, not
to mention the storm of tears, roughened her voice.

"Are you sure Mick means what he said?" I probed.

"He might change his mind, but I'm not going to change mine.
We're through!"

"You know your parents love you and so do Jim and I. You're
not alone."

"I know, but …all my plans. My dreams," she mourned. Then
sitting up straight she said, "Well, I'll just have to make other plans."

"Let's pray."

"Yeah, let's."

"God, Christina has some important decisions to make, and
she needs help. Please show her what the right decision is for her
and her baby. Amen."

A quick hug and a sniff and she left the office. How much
smaller—more vulnerable—she seems now. No defiance and stubborn self-confidence to puff her up. She is weighed down with fear
and betrayal. Mick has behaved just as badly as I expected. I'm so
glad she saw it for herself. My judging him would only have made
it more difficult for her to admit the truth.

By late spring, Mick had not changed his mind about adoption
nor had Christina changed hers about him. The baby was due in
a matter of weeks. What none of us realized was that God had
something special on His mind.

Camp Farthest Out™ (CFO), a House tradition, started in less than a week. This annual retreat held at Messiah College dominated our thoughts and prayers. "Lord, please make it possible for Christina to go to CFO with us," became our daily prayer. Because her due date was so close, Dr. Rowghani was reluctant to okay her participation, but the cool, aloof outsider had become an important part of our family. Finally, Dr. Rowghani gave his approval—Christina could go.

Hallelujahs rang in the family room when we got the good news. Excitement and anticipation hummed through the House—a week of laughter, learning, and relaxing was just ahead.

The evening worship had just ended, and our group was in a cluster talking about all that had happened during the second day of CFO when a man walked up to our group. He looked straight at Christina.

"I'm not sure why, but," he paused and shook his head. "I think God is telling me to give you something…I believe I'm supposed to give you a piano." He cleared his throat before continuing, "Would you, uh, would you like that?" His smile was tentative. He ran his hand through his hair, "Please don't think I'm nuts. I don't usually do things like this. But I felt God nudging me to give you a piano."

"You're not crazy," I reassured him. I looked at Jim, without a word, I knew we agreed. "God wants Christina to have a piano." I circled as much of her expanded waist as I could with my arm, "She plays beautifully."

"Really, Anne?" Christina asked. "God would do that for me?"

"Of course he would," Jim answered for both of us.

Tears glistened on cheeks creased by a big smile. Around the lump in her throat she shared a painful secret. "When my parents and I were fighting about Mick, I screamed at my dad 'I'm never going to play piano again.' So he sold it to pay some bills. A couple of weeks ago, he told me he was sorry it was gone, but he doesn't have the money to replace it."

Delighted, the man got an address and phone number promising that it would be delivered to her home.

The next day as Christina and I walked under some shimmering ash trees, she said, "Imagine God doing that for me! He loves me. And He went to all that trouble to give me a piano. It's awesome." She wrapped her arms around her rotund tummy and said, "All my questions and doubts about God just disappeared. Phfft!" She snapped her fingers. "He's real and He cares."

She wasn't the only one who found it easier to trust God. The girls enjoyed telling and retelling the story of the miracle piano. God had shown Himself to be real—and interested in them.

The day after we returned from CFO, Christina went into labor. With black, silky hair like Mick's, her nine-pound, five-ounce boy was as beautiful as any I had seen. Plump, dimpled fists rested on either side of his head and long, black lashes fluttered against his cheeks as he settled into slumber. Lord, I just know there is trouble ahead. No baby is easy to place in adoption, but a baby this adorable…Mick is sure to fight."

And he did. Mick came to see baby Nathan, whom Christina had named for her father, and then returned with his dad. On a third visit, he brought his mother. He insisted on holding his son each time. He informed Christina that he was going to raise his son, no matter what she wanted.

When Christina left the hospital, Nathan went into foster care. Mick was furious and immediately threatened legal action.

"Don't you dare try to give my son away!" he shouted into the phone after receiving the adoption release papers. "I won't sign, you hear me?"

"But it's best for Nathan. He'll have a loving home—a mother and a father…"

"You don't love him, but I do."

"No," Christina insisted, "I love him enough to give him the best future."

"Yeah, sure. You don't want him, but you have to find a petty excuse to dump him," Mick sneered. His voice hardened, "I'm going to raise my son." The slam of the receiver ended the conversation, and Christina came looking for me.

"What am I going to do?" Her voice trembled with fear and frustration. "I can't let Nathan go to a home like that."

Unfortunately, there wasn't much I could say to reassure her—biological parents do have first rights to custody. It would take an ugly courtroom fight to prove Mick an unfit father with no guarantee that the court would rule in Christina's favor.

Fortunately, the Calders knew their real Source of help and turned to Him for wisdom. As they prayed together, His direction became clear. They would welcome Christina and baby Nathan into their home. By helping Christina in this way, she could finish high school and train for a career. God's peace gave them the confidence that this was His plan.

Mick, unhappy with their decision, eventually filed for custody. He was unable to persuade the court that he could provide a more stable, loving home than the Calders. So, Nathan took Christina's last name and settled into a family that adored him.

Lord, it is awesome to watch You work—bringing healing to broken lives. Why You choose to use Jim and me as Your partners in this work I'll never understand, but thank You. There is joy and satisfaction beyond anything I could have imagined in being Your instruments. And You've made us grandparents in the ever-expanding family You are creating. You are awesome. You truly are.

Postscript

Christina finished high school and business school while her parents provided Nathan's childcare. She accepted a position as an executive secretary after graduation. She and her parents remained active in their church, and it was here that she met the man who would marry her and adopt Nathan. Mick gradually lost interest in his son and dropped out of the picture.

The Calders still support the House of His Creation even though it requires financial sacrifice to do so. They give so that other girls can receive the same guidance, care, and opportunity to heal that Christina had.

To think about

- God's restoration sometimes includes a miracle or two along the way.

- God shows Himself and His love for us in ways you and I could never dream of.

- God's plan for our lives and the lives of our children will unfold if we will only seek His will.

- When we are willing to obey His nudges, we can be part of God's expression of love to hurting, bewildered people.

"So I say to you:
Ask and it will be given to you;
seek and you will find;
knock and the door will be opened to you."

Luke 11:9

Chapter 15

The Next Step

Eight years—hard, wonderful years—had passed since we started the House of His Creation. Years filled with tears and joy, over two hundred "daughters," and innumerable miracles. Some of our girls stayed a few months; others were with us for more than a year. These were the ones, who after placing their babies for adoption, had no safe, loving home to return to. They were either estranged from their families or were unable to return because of abuse and neglect.

We couldn't just shove them out the door and say "good luck" simply because they were no longer pregnant. Some needed a stable family environment while emotional wounds healed. Some needed to complete their education. Others needed security and encouragement while they looked for work, and guidance as they moved toward financial and emotional independence.

But with up to five girls of the twelve not pregnant, that left room for just seven expectant mothers. Add the six who could receive care at the Lititz home, and the total was much less than the list of those wanting to come.

We needed a special after-care house. That way the two maternity homes could concentrate on pregnant girls, and we still wouldn't have to send girls away before they were ready. Our board prayed and deliberated and then agreed a second house should be built on the Coatesville property.

However, when they approached the bank, which already held mortgages on the two homes, they were denied. The loan officer did suggest another option—Jim and I would be eligible for a loan. This would work except for one small difficulty—we had no money.

Five years ago, we had made a charitable sale of the property to the ministry. So, we personally no longer had a mortgage, but working for a faith-based organization meant our salaries were small—and erratically paid. Our needs were always met, but we had no savings, nothing to use as collateral or a down payment.

Our board of directors found a solution. They deeded seven acres to us as a gift. That land provided the equity we needed to secure the loan. With the help of a cooperative, flexible builder and a swarm of eager volunteers, the house was completed in just six months.

More and more, our hearts were drawn to this new venture. By the time the house was completed, our decision was made—we would turn the maternity home over to new houseparents and take the challenge to develop an effective after-care program. Just two days before Christmas 1980, we moved into our new home along with Robin (who we considered our third daughter, because she had been with us from the earliest days of our ministry), Holly and Shelly (now sixteen and thirteen), and four new mothers who had placed their babies for adoption. What a wonderful Christmas present our new home was! In my imagination, I could see a giant bow perched on the rooftop, ribbon ends flowing down the front of the house and a gift tag which read:

To: Jim and Anne

    With Love, From: God

The basement housed our ministry offices, the first floor living quarters and the second floor bedrooms for five young women as well as our family. This meant twelve pregnant teens could receive nurture and support at the farmhouse. Rarely was there an empty bed in any of the three houses.

Our transition to after-care went smoothly, because Jim and I had talked and dreamed of this for much longer than the six months it had taken to build the house. The need for long-term care was so obvious. So many of our girls simply were not equipped to make it on their own. Finally, we had the needed space. So the new house was not so much a new direction as a more thorough and systematic approach to the after-care we had been trying to give all long.

And there were the young women who chose to raise their babies. They had all the same needs as the mothers who place in adoption plus one other very important one—safe, affordable child care. Watching Allison struggle to reach economic independence showed us just how difficult it was for young women from disadvantaged backgrounds to break free.

Yet another need and no program to meet it. We searched for homes in the community willing to take in one mother and child at a time. First we trained them in extended family living, before allowing them to experience the joys and frustrations of grandparenthood. The young mothers had the benefit of a caring family enthusiastic in their support of her goal to become self-sufficient. The babies had the benefit of double and triple the hugs and kisses, coos and cuddles.

If only there were enough families ready and willing to open their hearts to our young mothers. Even so, our goal remained to never release a young woman from our program without the support and encouragement she needed.

How Jim and I delighted to see our girls take those first attempts towards maturity—just as proud as new parents over a baby's first stumbling steps. Speaking engagements kept us busy and challenged. Neither burnout nor boredom had a foothold in our lives. We thoroughly enjoyed our lives and expected to grow old working at the House. But God had other plans.

Susan, one of the girls in the program, and I were in my office when Naomi, our secretary, buzzed me on the intercom. Since I had a very firm rule about no interruptions during a counseling session, I knew it had to be important and definitely out of the ordinary. "Yes, Naomi, what is it?"

"I'm sorry, Anne, but," Naomi sounded breathless and rattled. "You have a call on line one from the White House."

Susan's eyes widened. Calls from 1600 Pennsylvania Avenue were not an every day occurrence.

"The White House?" I parroted. Surely I had misunderstood or else one of our practical joking friends was pulling a prank. How Jim and some of our friends loved to 'put one over.' This can wait. I'll get to the bottom of it later. "Tell them we'll call them back," I told Naomi. "I'm busy with Susan right now."

Turning from the phone, I caught the awed expression on Susan's face. "You'd rather talk to me, than the president?" her voice squeaked on the last word.

"Sure!" I replied offhandedly smiling at her wide-eyed wonder. "I'm sure it's not the president, maybe a staff person. If it's important, I'll talk to them later."

Susan's self-esteem probably rose to new heights that afternoon, especially twenty minutes later when we discovered it really was the White House calling. Naomi chuckled as she relayed the message, "They are definitely not used to people calling them back. He was absolutely shocked that you didn't drop everything and everyone," she winked at Susan, "to take their call. He didn't say what he wanted. What is it about?"

"Haven't a clue," I said. "There's one way to find out." I took the note from her hand and dialed the number penciled on the memo. When I hang up the phone, my shock was as big as the staffer's had been. President Reagan wanted to mention us and The House of His Creation in a speech he would give before the National Religious Broadcasters. Would I give my permission? Yes, of course, he can! He went on to explain that the President believed Christian ministries like The House of His Creation provided positive examples for dealing with teen pregnancies, an area where government had proven itself ineffective. Wow, the President is going to cite our home as an example of a practical and effective response to one of society's critical problems!

The phone calls started almost immediately after the President's speech. From all over the country, requests came for ideas and help. People who felt God calling them to provide the same kind of care we give at The House, wanted us to come speak, advise, and encourage them.

With the memory of the last time I became deeply involved with the pro-life movement to the point of jeopardizing our own girls' well-being, I cautiously agreed to a few trips whenever my schedule allowed. But the requests far outnumbered my available days. How hard it was to turn down people who passionately wanted to start pro-life work in their area!

Then, President Reagan mentioned our House in his book, *Abortion and the Conscience of a Nation*. This led to two invitations to attend conferences in Washington, D.C., concerning the need for crisis pregnancy care nationwide.

We talked, listened, and became convinced that we could help develop the "care" portion of the pro-life movement. God was stretching our vision beyond our local area, beyond the state, to encompass the nation.

Conflict grew within me—one I recognized from previous experience. Supervising three homes, counseling and speaking packed my schedule to capacity...and yet, I had this compelling urge to help others get started.

It was time to pray, to find out where God wanted me to spend my time. I knew from lessons learned the hard way that He does not call me to an impossibly overcrowded schedule. We also began talking with our board about releasing us from direct supervision of the Homes. This would free us to concentrate on a ministry of consultation. Right in the middle of this time of prayer and searching, we faced one of the most difficult experiences of our ten years in ministry-a test that would either refine us or sideline us.

To think about

- God can open a door that will change our lives. All we have to do is walk through it.

- Fear, complacency, and busy-ness—they can keep us from opening our hearts and homes.

- When we are obedient today, God brings increase tomorrow—without our striving or manipulating.

"Sustain me, my God,
according to your promise,
and I will live;
do not let my hopes be dashed."

Psalm 119:116

Chapter 16

Robin

"I need to talk to you and Pop," Robin mumbled, unable to look at me. She had been alternately fidgeting and moping since she came home from work—something big was brewing. "In private, okay?"

She's going to tell us she wants to marry Chad. She knows we don't think he's the right one. She'll want our blessing anyway. What are we going to do?

"Right now?" I asked keeping my tone light—not an easy job considering the fast-rising anxiety inside me. A quick jerk of her head was her only reply. "Okay, let me get Jim. We'll meet you in the office."

Jim and Shelly were in the front yard gleefully stomping through piles of leaves. "Robin's waiting for us downstairs, and she's very nervous." Jim's eyebrows moved in a silent "uh-oh." As we walked I asked, "What are you going to say if she tells us she wants to marry Chad?"

"She's a grown woman," Jim reminded me. "What'll she be next birthday—twenty-five? We certainly can't stop her from marrying this guy."

Surely not twenty-five—why she was only fifteen when she arrived...oh dear, was it really ten years ago? And what a challenge she had been...

"Annie, it's the police. They found Robin in Virginia. We may lose her this time; she crossed state lines." Jim choked back tears, the product of mingled relief that Robin was found and despair that we might lose her. She had run away before—in fact, that was why she was placed with us originally. Habitually truant, the juvenile court was ready to send her to prison, but her grandmother had begged for her to be placed in a Christian home instead.

But running was the only way Robin knew how to cope with bad days at school or relationships that hurt. So she ran…and ran. How I had begged the Virginia judge for one more chance which grew into ten years of loving and disciplining and praying. She sanded and painted alongside us as we readied the farmhouse for living. She had slept on the floor just like the rest of us. And she had giggled with Holly and Shelly over Jim's latest practical jokes—how we loved this "third daughter" of ours!

We wanted so much more for her than what Chad offered— more than strikingly handsome features and an enticing "line." Robin might be enthralled with these, but I suspected Chad's only objective was sex, not the marriage she envisioned. Because they worked in the same mall, he had had plenty of opportunities to spin his web.

Why can't Robin see him for what he is—a self-absorbed, shallow, showy young man who still has a lot of growing up to do? Robin knew Chad did not impress us, but she insisted we just didn't know him well enough. "There are just so many wonderful things about him."

I prayed again as Jim and I had repeatedly prayed. Lord, please spare Robin from any serious harm from this man. Open her eyes, please… We saw the tears as soon as we entered the office. Sitting down facing Robin, we braced ourselves for whatever distressing news she had to share. "What did you want to see us about?" I asked quietly.

"I'm pregnant!" she blurted out, then rushed on. "I'm leaving! I know you're upset. Don't worry. I'm getting married…" Sobs punctuated each word. She never once looked at us, just cried while Jim and I sat stunned…silent…frozen. I never considered…I thought…What will people think? Holly and Shelly, what will they think? Oh no, the ministry…our reputation…people will say we're unfit…how could she do this to us? The last of these tumbling thoughts yanked me out of my downward spiral. Robin hadn't done this to hurt us. Stop thinking about yourself, Anne. Robin is hurting.

My poor, frantic daughter. No wonder she had been moody— what a burden to carry. A glance at Jim told me how deeply he hurt, tears leaked from the corner of his eye and wandered down his cheek. He made no attempt to wipe it away. I swallowed hard, pushing down my own pain and injured pride. "Okay, Robin, calm down now," I kept my voice soft and low, treating the situation as gingerly as if I was handling cracked eggs, "Let's take this one step at a time."

Jim's voice broke, "You know we love you, don't you?" Robin's nod was interrupted by her hiccuping sob. His chest heaved as he tried to speak around his tears, "You don't have to get married."

"You are our precious daughter. We want the best for you," I whispered. My tears spilled faster than any tissue could absorb. I continued to talk and listen, but it seemed unreal. I was wrapped in fog—separated, distant, every movement an effort.

Minutes dragged by as we hurt and cried and talked. Finally emotions exhausted, I hugged Robin tightly and said, "You've been thinking about this for a while, but we haven't. Please give us time to adjust."

Robin quivered. Her whisper so low I wouldn't have heard it if she hadn't been resting her head on my shoulder, "Okay."

"We need time to sleep and think," I continued. "Let's plan to talk tomorrow evening—with Chad." The next couple of days were a blur. Hurt and disappointment threatened to overwhelm me. Every time I was alone, I cried. Jim turned to a pastor friend, Jack Crans, who often provided a combination sounding board and personal advisor. They wept, and Jack interceded, asking the Lord to help Jim deal with his pain.

As Jim and I talked, we both concluded that a hasty marriage was not in Robin's best interest. The unplanned pregnancy had not changed Chad—he remained irresponsible, and unconcerned. At 28, he still lived with his parents. No plans for the future. No ambition. No desire to change.

If we could just buy enough time for Robin to see that this was not a marriage made in heaven, we could save her so much heartache. We asked them to go to Jack for pre-marital counseling. They agreed. Jim and I prayed...and prayed.

In the meantime, we both told Robin how pleased and proud we were that she hadn't considered the "easy way" out of the situation. But then she had been there when Meredith and Angie told their stories and shared their pain. She knew abortion was anything but easy. Regardless of whatever other decisions, wise or foolish, that Robin made, she would not have to carry that burden of regret and guilt.

There were more than enough negative emotions surging and saturating our household: self-incrimination, fear, anger, helplessness and embarrassment took turns pummeling Jim and me. Meredith's mother had been right when she said, "You don't know how it feels." Now we did. Like all Christian parents, we wondered,

Where are you, God, in all of this? Are You really here with us? Why did You let this happen? We've prayed and prayed! You're allowing our parenting skills to be discredited after we've devoted our lives to a ministry You inspired. We questioned ourselves: What had we done wrong? We worried about the future: What impact would this have on the ministry?

Slowly, we realized God had not caused these events. Robin possessed the same free will God had given to everyone—she, like the girls who came to the House for maternity care, had chosen to become sexually active. She didn't do it to punish us or hurt our ministry. She yielded to her infatuation for Chad and pregnancy was the consequence. I have noticed that God often allows a pregnancy to bring inappropriate sexual activity to light.

Our input into Robin's decision was limited. We had taught her God's plan for marriage. We had modeled husband and wife roles for her. We had given her as much counsel as she would receive. Ultimately, Robin would make her own choice. We could cheerlead and coach, but only from the sidelines. After telling other parents this painful reality, we were experiencing it ourselves.

When Chad and Robin asked Pastor Jack to marry them, he declined with a heavy heart. He told them their marriage had little chance for success. One week later, Robin called while I was washing the supper dishes. "It's done. We're married. I'm coming by later for my things."

Five dollars for a license, a visit to the district justice, and our Robin was a married woman. We tried to be happy for her. We hoped we were wrong about their future together. Still, sadness pooled in our hearts as we watched her pack all her clothes and possessions to move them to Chad's parents' house.

We gained a new understanding of the strain an unplanned pregnancy puts on a family—the forces at work to tear it apart or bond it together depending on the family's response. We discovered our love did not shrink or fade, but our responsibility and control did. When their son Brandon was born, Jim and I rejoiced with them, but they were out of our keeping. We learned to entrust them to God's care. Letting go is not an easy lesson to master. Out of our experience came a greater compassion for the pain of parents and grandparents—we ministered with more sensitivity and effectiveness. A new urgency to minister to the whole family was birthed within us.

In the end, Jim and I were more certain than ever that God had called us to this work. Our experience with Robin had only deepened our desire to help others in similar circumstances. God had enabled us to deal lovingly and rationally with Robin's situation—we had been comforted so that we, in turn, could comfort.

We have no easy answers for preventing unplanned pregnancies, but we have God's love and grace, which enable us to cope— one girl at a time—with the problems that come.

Postscript

Robin's marriage to Chad lasted three years before ending in divorce. We know God is not through with Robin. We continue to ask Him to complete the work He began in her and to give her a life's companion of His own choosing.

To think about

- It's one thing to help others; it's another thing to make their problems your own. God is still God, and His promises will work for others just as they have worked for you.

- Consequences tag along after our choices—trying to run from them only produces bigger repercussions.

- Trusting God always requires letting go.

- We cannot focus on our pain and at the same time help some one else cope with theirs. How much better to comfort someone else rather than dwell on our own hurts.

- Handle volatile situations as if you were handling nitroglycerin—with caution and respect.

"Because of the service by which you have proved yourselves,
others will praise God for the obedience that accompanies
your confession of the gospel of Christ,
and for your generosity in sharing with them
and with everyone else."

2 Corinthians 9:13

Chapter 17

Ending So That
We Can Begin

The call to provide teaching and assistance to fledgling pro-life ministries nationwide became stronger and stronger. By the spring of 1984, that call had become imperative. As much as we loved our work at the House of His Creation, as deep as our friendship and fellowship with the staff and board, we realized we must let go to take this new step of faith.

This time of transition was also a time of transformation. File drawers crammed with the worksheets I had designed and used with the girls were being compiled for publication. These sheets, filled with questions, and a few carefully worded facts, helped my girls find God's plans and purposes for themselves and their babies. Titled My Baby and Me, this workbook series could be used by new homes and ministries all across the country.

As always, where God leads, He provides. The first printing was donated by the printer and the sale of that first printing covered the start-up costs of our new ministry, Loving and Caring, Inc. Office space was given rent-free by Joe and Kathleen Anders, a Christian counselor and his wife.

From that small beginning, God has "grown" and prospered Loving and Caring. Today, it includes consultation services; adoption, counseling, and fatherlessness seminars; personnel retreats and training, as well as an increasing array of materials and re-sources.

I miss The House and my role as mother to girls like Melissa, Allison, Meredith, Christina, and Robin. I especially miss the one-on-one contact with women and their families. Jim misses the interaction with the girls, the birthfathers and fathers, but we realize that season is over. The Lord has filled our lives with so many new challenges and friends that we don't look back, except to smile at all the wonderful memories. We had eleven incredible years to learn, love, and serve frightened young women facing a crisis pregnancy. Now we take our experience and share it with a much wider audience. We continue to trust God for all we need. God's provisions for our necessities are always on time. We serve a powerful and generous God who delights in blessing us.

To think about

- God brings people into our lives with special gifts just when we need them. From the gifts come special friend-ships.

- One friend sacrificing for another—this truly blesses the heart of God.

- Small beginnings do not mean small results.

- The greatest satisfaction in life is not a large bank account or a prestigious job. It is obedience to God's call. For it is in the center of His will that we find both awesome adventures and an inexhaustible well of joy.

Epilogue

The Multiplication Factor

"There's a call on line one for you, Anne."

It was 2005, and I was back at The House of His Creation as interim director. It was a wonderful opportunity for me to interact with young women every day.

"Hello, this is Anne Pierson. How can I help you?"

"My name is Kelly, and I was hoping you could tell me about my birth mother. According to my birth certificate, she was at the House of His Creation twenty-two years ago when I was born." The voice on the other end was soft and hesitant.

Over and over God has orchestrated events in my life in incredible ways. And every time, it sends a thrill up my spine! When I accepted the position of interim director, I discovered over twenty years of client folders in disorganized heaps. Just two days ago, I had filed the last one.

If I hadn't taken the position…if I hadn't tackled that back log of manila folders…and if I hadn't spent the extra hours to get it done…the information Kelly needed would have been buried in a dusty avalanche and inaccessible. But now it was a simple matter of opening the right filing cabinet and pulling out the right folder.

Thank you, Father, for ordering my steps.

As soon as I opened Kelly's file, I remembered her mother— bright copper curls and a lilting brogue.

"My adoptive parents knew I was part Irish. In fact, my father made sure I got to Irish festivals and dance productions. I want to spend time in Ireland, but to do that I need to prove Irish ancestry."

"That shouldn't be difficult; your birth mother was an Irish citizen. Would you like to meet her if she wants to make contact?"

"I guess so...I don't want to do something that will hurt my parents. I've never had a terrible need to know her or my birthfather. But if it can be arranged..."

In the end, Kelly met not only her birthmother, but her birthfather—in Ireland—as well. Since she is Irish on both sides, getting permission to live in Ireland for six months was not a problem.

Jim and I had dinner and phone conversations with Kelly and her new husband, Tim, several times since they returned to the United States. Not long ago, they shared their good-news—a baby boy was due to arrive in six months.

The impact of our choices keeps getting larger, not smaller, over time. If Kelly's mother had not chosen life, then not only would her adoptive family and Tim have missed out, but there would be no baby on the way. Three generations—and counting—have been changed by that one choice.

Father, thank You for reminding me yet again that our seeds of obedience keep yielding harvest after harvest. For that same reason, I don't ever want to sow seeds of disobedience—I don't want multiplying harvests of weeds and thistles!

To think about

- Just how much impact does one ordinary life make?

- What decisions did members of my family make that affect you today?

- What seeds of obedience are busy multiplying in your life?

- God is the master of networking. When people "happen" across our path, His Hand is at work.

**For more copies of this book
or to contact us**

www.lovingandcaring.org
mail@lovingandcaring.org
717-293-3230

Made in the USA
Middletown, DE
01 February 2017